INDEX

ENGINE TROUBLES

ELECTRICAL TROUBLES

CLUTCH TROUBLES

RAMBLER "E-STICK" TROUBLES

SYNCHROMESH TRANSMISSION TROUBLES

OVERDRIVE TROUBLES

Diagnosis

Mechanical

AUTOMATIC TRANSMISSION TROUBLES
GENERAL MOTORS UNITS

CHRYSLER UNITS

FORD UNITS

MISCELLANEOUS

REAR AXLE TROUBLES

DRUM BRAKE TROUBLES

DISC BRAKES TROUBLES

POWER BRAKE TROUBLES

FRONT END & STEERING TROUBLES

POWER STEERING TROUBLES

POWER TOP, WINDOW & SEAT TROUBLES

Hydro-Lectric Type

Electric Type for Windows & Seats

WINDSHIELD WIPER TROUBLES

AIR CONDITIONING

AUTOMATIC LEVEL CONTROL
GENERAL MOTORS

FORD MOTOR COMPANY

SPEED CONTROLS

▶ ENGINE TROUBLES

STARTING A STALLED ENGINE

When an engine fails to start the chances are that 90 per cent of the cases will involve the ignition system and seldom the fuel system or other miscellaneous reasons. If a systematic procedure is followed the trouble can almost always be found without the use of special equipment.

To begin with, turn on the ignition switch and if the ammeter shows a slight discharge (or if the telltale lamp lights) it indicates that current is flowing. A glance at the gas gauge will indicate whether or not there is fuel in the tank.

Operate the starter and if the engine turns over freely, both the battery and starter are functioning properly. On the other hand, if the starter action is sluggish it may be due to a discharged or defective battery, loose corroded or dirty battery terminals, mechanical failure in the starter, starter switch or starter drive. If the starter circuit is okay, skip this phase of the discussion and proceed to ignition.

Starter Circuit Checkout

To determine which part of the starter circuit is at fault, turn on the light switch and again operate the starter. Should the lights go out or become dim, the trouble is either in the battery, its connections or cables. A hydrometer test of the battery should indicate better than 1.250 specific gravity, while a voltmeter placed across the positive and negative posts, should indicate about 6 volts for a 6-volt battery and 12 volts for a 12-volt system. If either of these tests prove okay, clean and tighten the battery connections and cable terminals or replace any cable which seems doubtful.

If the lights remain bright when the starter is operated, the trouble is between the battery and the starter, or the starter switch is at fault, since it is evident that there is no electrical connection between these points. If these connections are clean and tight, it is safe to assume that the starter or starter switch is defective.

Neutral Safety Switch

If the ammeter shows a slight discharge (or if the telltale lamp lights) when the ignition is turned on, but the system goes dead when the starting circuit is closed, the neutral safety switch may be at fault. To check, bypass the switch with a suitable jumper. If the engine now starts, adjust or replace the switch.

CAUTION: With the safety switch bypassed, the car can be started in any gear. *Be sure the transmission is in neutral or park and the parking brake is applied.*

Primary Ignition Checkout

Let's assume that the battery and starter are doing their job, and that fuel is reaching the carburetor, but the car does not start, then the trouble must be somewhere in the ignition circuit. But first, before starting your diagnosis, it is advisable to give the whole system a visual inspection which might uncover obvious things such as broken or disconnected wires etc.

The best way to start tracking down ignition troubles is to begin with the primary circuit since this is where troubles show up most frequently. First remove the distributor cap and block the points open with a piece of cardboard, then turn on the ignition and with a test bulb or voltmeter check to see if there is current at the terminal on the distributor. If you do not get a reading at this point, the current is cut off somewhere in the connections leading back to the ignition switch or it may be that the condenser has an internal short to the ground. The latter possibility can be eliminated if you can restore current at the distributor terminal by disconnecting the condenser from the distributor plate so that its outside shell is not grounded. With the possibility of a bad condenser out of the way, work toward the ignition switch and test for current at each connection until you get to one where you get a reading. Between this connection and the distributor lies the trouble.

On cars with 12-volt systems, that have an external ignition coil ballast resistor, the foregoing steps in checking the primary circuit should include checking the ignition coil resistor for defects or loose connections. As this is done, bear in mind that while the starter cranks the engine, the resistor is by-passed by the starter switch on Ford and Delco-Remy systems. This means that while the circuit through the resistor may be satisfactory, a broken connection or high resistance between the starter switch by-pass terminal and the coil would prevent starting. On the other hand, a satisfactory by-pass circuit might start the engine while the engine would stall immediately upon releasing the starter switch if there was a defect in the coil resistance circuit.

If, to begin with, the test equipment shows a current reading at the distributor terminal, it is safe to assume that the trouble is in the unit itself, most likely burned or dirty breaker points. A final positive test for defective breaker points can be made very simply by removing the cardboard from between the points, and positioning the distributor cam by turning the engine to where the points are closed. With the points closed there should be no current at the distributor terminal. If there is current replace the points.

In an emergency, the points can be cleaned by using the sanded side of a match box, a knife blade, or the sharp edge of a screwdriver to scrape the scale from the contact faces. After cleaning the points, and a gauge is not available to set the gap, a quick adjustment can be made by using four layers of a piece of newspaper. The thickness of the paper is equivalent to about .020″, which is the approximate gap setting for most distributors. Of course, at the earliest opportunity, a precise point adjustment should be made.

If the procedure outlined under "Primary Ignition Checkout" does not uncover the trouble then it will be necessary to continue the tests into the secondary ignition circuit.

Secondary Ignition Checkout

First of all, remove the wire from one of the spark plugs, turn on the ignition and operate the starter. While the engine is cranking, hold the terminal of the spark plug wire about ¼″ away from the engine or spark plug base. If the spark is strong and jumps the gap, the trouble is confined to either the spark plugs or lack of fuel. Before going any further, wipe the outside of the plugs to remove any dirt or dampness which would create an easy path for the current to flow, then try to start the engine again. If it still fails to start, remove one of the spark plugs and if it is wet around the base, it indicates that the fuel system is okay, so it naturally follows that the spark plugs are at fault. Remove all the plugs, clean them and set the gaps. An emergency adjustment of spark plug gaps can be made by folding a piece of newspaper into five layers. When changing the gap, always bend the side (ground) electrode and never the center one as there is danger of breaking the insulation.

Fuel System Checkout

If the spark plug that was removed showed no indication of dampness on its base, check the fuel system. A quick check can be made by simply removing the carburetor air cleaner and looking down into the carburetor. Open and close the throttle manually and if fuel is present in the carburetor, the throttle will operate the accelerating pump, causing it to push gasoline through the pump jet. If it does, check the choke valve. If the engine is cold, the choke valve should be closed. If the choke won't close, the engine can be started by covering the carburetor throat with your hand while the engine is cranking, provided, of course, that fuel is reaching the carburetor.

Check the operation of the fuel pump by disconnecting the fuel lines from the pump to the carburetor. Crank the engine and if the pump is working, fuel will pulsate out of the line. If not, either the pump isn't working or the line from the tank to the pump is clogged. Before blaming the pump, however, disconnect the line at the inlet side of the pump which leads to the tank and, while a companion listens at the tank, blow through the line. If a gurgling sound is heard back in the tank, the line is open and the trouble is in the pump. Remove the sediment bowl and clean the screen, then replace the bowl and screen, being sure that you have an air-tight fit. If the pump still refuses to function, it should be removed and repaired.

The foregoing discussion will, in most cases, uncover the cause of why an engine won't start. However, if further diagnosis is necessary, the following list will undoubtedly provide the answer.

ENGINE WON'T START

Important—Alternator equipped cars cannot be push-started when the battery is completely dead because, unlike a generator, there is no residual magnetism in the rotor.

If the engine fires when the ignition switch is turned on but quits when the switch is released to its running position, it indicates that the ignition coil resistor has lost its continuity or there is a bad connection at the resistor terminals.

Due to Open Primary Ignition Circuit

1. Burned or oxidized ignition points.
2. Ignition coil resistance unit burned out or open (12 Volt systems).
3. Starting switch ignition coil resistance by-pass circuit open (12 Volt systems).
4. Ignition points not closing.
5. Breaker arm binding on pivot post, preventing closing of points.
6. Breaker arm spring weak or broken.
7. Breaker arm distorted or bent.
8. Dirty ignition points.
9. Primary lead connection loose at distributor or coil.
10. Primary windings in coil broken.
11. Open ignition switch circuit.

Due to Grounded Primary Ignition Circuit

A grounded coil primary winding, a grounded ignition switch, or a grounded switch-to-coil primary lead will cause excessive current flow and will usually cause wires to burn.

1. Ignition points not opening or closing due to improper adjustment.
2. Ignition points not opening due to worn rubbing block on breaker arm.
3. Faulty insulating bushing in breaker arm.
4. Cracked or faulty insulator at distributor primary terminal.
5. Grounded condenser.
6. Distributor-to-coil lead grounded.
7. Primary coil winding grounded.

Due to Faulty Secondary Ignition Circuit

1. Corroded spark plug cable terminals.
2. Chafed or cracked insulation on cables.
3. Ignition coil weak or inoperative.
4. Moisture on ignition coil, terminals, distributor cover, spark plug porcelains, or in distributor.
5. Improper type of spark plugs.
6. Cracked distributor cap or a burned carbon track from distributor cap center terminal to distributor housing.
7. Improper installation of spark plug cable (not correct for engine firing order).
8. Spark plugs damaged, dirty or wet, porcelains cracked, or gaps improperly spaced.
9. Rotor contact spring bent or broken.
10. Distributor rotor grounded.
11. Distributor cap center terminal (inner) broken or missing.
12. Broken or burned out radio suppressor in distributor cap.

Due to Battery

1. Battery run down.
2. Terminals loose or badly corroded.
3. Improper ground.
4. Battery cables frayed or undersize.

Due to Starter Motor

1. Not operating properly.
2. Congealed engine oil due to use of too heavy a grade of oil or to the formation of sludge.
3. Starter gear binding in flywheel gear.
4. Defective starter switch.
5. Faulty neutral safety switch on cars with automatic transmission.

Due to Excessive Fuel Supply (Flooding)

The engine is said to be flooded with fuel when a quantity of liquid fuel collects in the intake manifold, and perhaps also in the cylinders. This condition gives a mixture that is much too rich to ignite.

If the carburetor has a provision for opening the choke valve when the throttle is fully open, crank the engine with the throttle open until engine starts. It will start as soon as the extra fuel is pumped out.

If the choke valve is not designed to open when the throttle is fully opened, tie or block the choke valve open and crank the engine until it starts.

Flooding may also occur on the road. If the carburetor supplies too rich a mixture at full throttle, the intake manifold may be flooded with liquid fuel, with the result that when the engine is stopped, heat evaporates the fuel and thus provides an over-rich incombustible mixture. The engine won't start until the rich mixture is pumped out by cranking.

1. Choke not operating properly.
2. Automatic choke not properly set.

3. Carburetor unloader linkage (if equipped) not properly set.
4. Float level set too high.
5. Dirty, worn or faulty needle valve and seat.
6. Float sticking or rubbing against side of fuel bowl.
7. Leak in float, allowing fuel to get inside.
8. Fuel pump pressure too great.

Due to Insufficient Fuel Supply

1. Carburetor inlet needle stuck in its seat, due to gum in fuel.
2. Float level too low.
3. Clogged inlet screen at carburetor.
4. Faulty fuel pump or one of insufficient capacity.
5. Fuel pump strainer clogged.
6. Faulty fuel pump bowl gasket.
7. Flexible line (if used) twisted, deteriorated or restricted.
8. Fuel line to tank clogged, kinked, restricted.
9. Vent in fuel tank filler cap clogged or restricted.
10. Worn fuel pump camshaft lobe.

HARD STARTING

When Engine is Hot

This condition is usually caused by an over-supply of fuel due to any of the items listed under *Engine Won't Start Due to Excessive Fuel Supply*. In rare cases, an ignition coil may lose its efficiency when it is hot and cause ignition failure.

When Engine is Cold

Many of the conditions enumerated under *Engine Won't Start* also may cause hard starting in cold weather. Of particular importance, however, are the following:

1. Choke setting too lean.
2. Fuel may have kerosene in it or water, or ice in bottom of tank.
3. Ice in fuel filter bowl.

4. Ice in fuel lines.
5. Engine is cranked too slowly or won't turn over because: (a) engine oil is too thick in sub-zero weather; (b) battery weak due to extremely low temperature.
6. Another possibility, although remote, is that the water pump is jammed with ice, which will interfere with cranking engine if fan belt is tight.

Due to Vapor Lock

The term vapor lock means the flow of fuel to the mixing chamber in the carburetor has been stopped (locked) by the formation of vaporized fuel pockets or bubbles caused by over-heating the fuel by hot fuel pump, hot fuel lines or hot carburetor.

The more volatile the fuel the greater the tendency for it to vapor lock. Vapor lock is encouraged by high atmospheric temperature, hard driving, defective engine cooling and high altitude.

A mild case of vapor lock will cause missing and hard starting when engine is warm. Somewhat more severe vapor lock will stop the engine which cannot be started again until it has cooled off enough so that any vaporized fuel has condensed to a liquid.

Service Note: Some cars equipped with air conditioning have a vapor bypass system. These cars have a special fuel filter which has a metering outlet in the top. Any vapor which forms is bled off and returned to the fuel tank through a separate line alongside the fuel supply line. This system greatly reduces the possibility of vapor lock. However, if vapor lock is suspected examine the by-pass valve to see if it is functioning.

Due to Percolation

Percolation means simply that gasoline in the carburetor bowl is boiling over into the intake manifold. This condition is most apt to occur immediately after a hot engine is shut off.

Most carburetors have a provision for relieving the vapor pressure of overheated fuel in the carburetor bowl by means of ports. If, however, percolation should take place, the engine may be started by allowing it to cool slightly and then holding the throttle wide open while cranking to clear the intake manifold of excess fuel.

After Long Storage

1. The more volatile components in the fuel have evaporated and those remaining are not sufficiently volatile to provide a combustible mixture.
2. Low or run-down battery.
3. Corrosion of engine parts may result in so much friction that starter cannot crank engine at proper speed, if at all.
4. Pistons, etc. may be stuck fast by gummy oil.
5. Engine valves may stick open due to gummy deposits.
6. There is the possibility that any small part essential to the running of the engine may be stuck due to gummy film or to corrosion.
7. Some of these troubles are most likely to occur in hot, humid climate and near salt water.

ENGINE STALLS

Many troubles which prevent smooth running at idle may cause stalling. The list includes almost everything that may cause hard starting or missing. Some of the more common causes are:

1. Engine idle speed set too low.
2. Large air leaks in intake manifold such as a disconnected windshield wiper vacuum line.
3. Ignition points need attention.
4. Vapor lock.
5. Over-supply of fuel (flooding).
6. Valves set too tight.

If carburetor is equipped with a fast idle cam, which increases engine speed when the choke is in operation during the warm-up period, the engine may stall if the fast idle device fails to open the throttle due to sticking or need for adjustment.

On some cars equipped with a fluid coupling or torque converter, if the throttle is closed quickly the engine stalls. To avoid this trouble, most cars have a device which retards the speed of the throttle closing; this is called a throttle return check or dashpot and is usually mounted on the carburetor. It consists of a piston or diaphragm and a spring-closed check valve. If the linkage is out of adjustment or the check valve leaks, the engine will stall.

If the engine quits smoothly when car is in operation, the trouble is often caused by sudden lack of fuel due to:

1. Fuel tank empty.
2. Vapor lock.
3. Flooding.
4. Water in fuel.
5. Frozen fuel line.

Carburetor Icing

The carburetor discharges liquid fuel into the air stream in the form of an atomized spray which evaporates readily. The heat required to evaporate the gasoline is drawn from the entering air, thereby lowering its temperature. The cooler air chills the interior of the carburetor and may cause the moisture in the air to condense into droplets.

Under certain conditions of atmospheric temperature and humidity, the liberated moisture actually collects and freezes on the chilled carburetor surfaces, especially on the throttle plate and surrounding throttle body. When the throttle is almost completely closed for idling, this ice tends to bridge the gap between the throttle plate and throttle body, thereby cutting off the air supply and causing the engine to stall. Opening the throttle for restarting breaks the ice bridge but does not eliminate the possibility of further stalling until the engine and carburetor have warmed up.

For carburetor icing to occur, the outside air must be cool enough so that the refrigerating effect of fuel evaporation in the carburetor will lower the temperatures of the throttle plate and body below both the dew point of moist air and the freezing point of water. The air must also contain sufficient moisture for appreciable condensation of water to occur when it is chilled in the carburetor.

Generally speaking, carburetor icing occurs when winter grade gasoline (more volatile than summer grade) is used and when the atmospheric temperature ranges from 30° to 50° F. at relative humidities in excess of 65%.

Carburetor icing problems can be reduced by the use of anti-icing additives, such as alcohols, in the fuel. Some fuel refiners use anti-stalling additives in their gasolines which have proved effective in combating carburetor icing.

Another form of carburetor icing has been observed in some engines during high-speed driving on cool, moist days. When certain cars are driven steadily at 60 to 80 mph, the large quantities of cool air passing through the carburetor may result in gradual ice formation within the carburetor's venturi. Since this ice restricts the venturi passage, the resultant increased vacuum in the venturi tends to increase the rate of fuel flow. The fuel-air mixture thus becomes excessively rich, causing loss of power and high fuel consumption.

ENGINE STARTS BUT WON'T DRIVE CAR

1. Broken part in the drive line anywhere from clutch to rear axle shaft.
2. No oil or not enough oil in fluid coupling or torque converter.
3. Some defect in automatic transmission causes binding or dragging of clutches or slipping bands.
4. Engine develops only enough power to run itself due to: (a) extremely lean or rich mixture; (b) excessive engine friction; (c) throttle does not

open; (d) very dirty air cleaner; (e) clogged exhaust system.

5. Oil in fluid coupling or torque converter is semi-
solid due to zero temperature. This trouble is un-
likely if the recommended oil is used.

ENGINE MISFIRES

At All Speeds

1. Fouled spark plug or broken porcelain.
2. Faulty spark plug cables.
3. Low battery voltage.
4. Low generator voltage.
5. Burned or pitted ignition points.
6. Incorrect ignition point gap.
7. Faulty condenser or coil.
8. Weak spark or no spark in one or more cylinders.
9. Faulty distributor cap or rotor.
10. Primary circuit restricted or open intermittently.
11. Primary circuit detoured by short intermittently.
12. Secondary circuit restricted or open intermittently.
13. Secondary circuit detoured by short intermittently.
14. Blown cylinder head gasket between cylinders.
    This can be noted when missing occurs in two
    adjacent cylinders.
15. Sticking valves.
16. Hydraulic tappet holds valve open slightly.
17. Broken valve spring.
18. Leak at intake manifold gaskets.
19. Mixture too rich or too lean.

At High Speed

1. Hot spark plugs. Change to colder type but note
   that a hot plug may be due to loose installation or
   lack of a plug gasket (if gasket is called for).
2. Ignition point gap much too wide.
3. Breaker arm binding or sticking.
4. Breaker arm spring weak.

5. Sticking engine valves.
6. Valve springs too weak to close valves promptly.
7. Valve springs broken.
8. Valve springs shimmy.
9. Intermittent delivery of fuel to carburetor so that momentarily the mixture is too weak for combustion.
10. Mild vapor lock.
11. Weak spark.
12. Exhaust manifold clogged with carbon.
13. Exhaust manifold, muffler or tail pipe restricted.
14. Improper ignition timing.
15. Centrifugal advance not functioning properly.
16. Manifold heater valve held closed.
17. Dirty carburetor air cleaner.
18. Choke valve not completely open.
19. Carburetor throttle lever loose on shaft.
20. Improper fuel pump operation.
21. Pre-ignition.
22. Incorrect valve timing.

At Low or Idle Speeds

1. Faulty spark plugs.
2. Spark plug gaps too narrow.
3. Dirty or corroded secondary circuit connections or faulty ignition cables.
4. Cracked or faulty distributor cap. Radial contacts in cap burned or worn.
5. Dirty air cleaner.
6. Leaky valves.
7. Ignition point gap too narrow.
8. Faulty carburetion due to: (a) float level too high or too low; (b) float valve leaking; (c) incorrect or loose jets; (d) restricted or partially clogged idle air passage or jet; (e) air leak occurring between upper and lower carburetor body; (f) air leak occurring around carburetor throttle shaft.

9. Air leaks in intake manifold or carburetor resulting from: (a) loose manifold connections or leaks occurring in vacuum lines; (b) loose manifold nuts or capscrews; (c) broken or damaged intake manifold or carburetor gaskets; (d) cracked manifold; (e) warped or damaged manifold contacting surface.

10. Slight leaks occurring at fuel pump check valves.

11. Air leak occurring around intake valve stem because of excessive valve stem-to-guide clearance.

When Car is Accelerated

If the engine misses when car is accelerated but does not miss when idling the reason is that the spark plugs stop firing because of increased compression pressure caused by:

1. Weak spark.
2. Plug gaps too wide.
3. Plug fouled or damp.
4. Plug porcelain below par.
   Also see FLAT SPOT.

LACK OF POWER OR HIGH SPEED PERFORMANCE

It should be noted that the altitude at which the car is operated has a decided effect on performance. A car adjusted for normal altitudes will lack performance at high altitudes, whereas a car which operates normally at high altitudes may have a lean carburetor adjustment and show signs of pre-ignition when operated at sea level.

1. Ignition timing incorrect.
2. Centrifugal governor advance not operating properly.
3. Vacuum advance not operating properly.
4. Ignition points burned, pitted, sticking or bouncing (due to weak breaker arm spring).
5. Faulty spark plugs.
6. Faulty ignition cables.

7. Faulty ignition coil.
8. Faulty carburetion.
9. Lack of engine compression.
10. Pre-ignition.
11. Inoperative manifold heater valve (stuck closed).
12. Restricted carburetor inlet resulting from dirty air cleaner or choke valve not fully open.
13. Carburetor throttle lever loose on shaft.
14. Throttle linkage not properly adjusted.
15. Carburetor throttle valve not completely open.
16. Carburetor accelerating pump not functioning properly.
17. Improper fuel pump operation.
18. Partially restricted exhaust pipe, muffler or tail pipe.
19. Clutch slippage.
20. Excessive rolling resistance resulting from (a) dragging brakes, (b) tight wheel bearings, (c) misalignment of power transmitting units, (d) misalignment of rear axle, (e) underinflated tires.
21. Incorrect rear axle gear ratio.
22. Oversize tires.
23. Incorrect valve timing.
24. Inaccurate speedometer (gives impression of lack of performance).

ROUGH IDLE

The term "rough idle" means that the engine does not run smoothly when idling. The most likely cause is an over-rich mixture but any defect which produces uneven explosions or missing will cause a rough idle. The most common causes are:

1. Dirty idle jets and passages.
2. Improper idle adjustment.
3. Dirty air cleaner.
4. Improper float level.

5. Choke set too rich.
6. Air leak into intake manifold.
7. Clogged idle jets.
8. Improper ignition point gap.
9. Improper spark plug gap.
10. Weak spark.
11. Leaky engine valve.
12. Sticking valve or rocker arm.
13. Broken valve spring.
14. Insufficient tappet clearance.
15. Improper fuel pump pressure.
16. Sticking breaker arm.
17. Hydraulic tappet holds valve open.
18. Fuel volatility too high or too low.

SPARK KNOCK, PING, DETONATION

All three expressions mean the same thing. It is a sharp metallic knock caused by vibration of the cylinder head and block. The vibration is due to split-second high-pressure waves resulting from almost instantaneous abnormal combustion instead of the slower normal combustion.

The ping may be mild or loud. A mild ping does no harm but a severe ping will reduce power. A very severe ping may shatter spark plugs, break valves or crack pistons.

Pinging is most likely to occur on open throttle at low or moderate engine speed. Pinging is encouraged by:

1. Overheated engine.
2. Low octane fuel.
3. Too high compression.
4. Spark advanced too far.
5. Hot mixture due to hot engine or hot weather.
6. Heavy carbon deposit which increases the compression pressure.

Tendency to ping increases with mixture temperature including high atmospheric temperature; intake manifold heater valve "on" when engine is warm; hot cooling water;

hot interior engine surfaces due to sluggish water circulation or water jackets clogged with rust or dirt especially around exhaust valves. Some of these troubles may be confined to one or two cylinders.

If an engine pings objectionably because of too low octane fuel, retard the spark setting but first be sure that the cooling system is in good condition, the mixture not too lean and the combustion chambers free of carbon deposit.

PRE-IGNITION

Pre-ignition means that the mixture is set on fire before the spark occurs, being ignited by a red hot spot in the combustion chamber such as an incandescent particle of carbon; a thin piece of protruding metal; an over-heated spark plug, or a bright red hot exhaust valve. The result is reduction of power and over-heating accompanied by pinging. The bright red hot exhaust valve may be due to a leak, to lack of tappet clearance, to valve sticking, or a weak or broken spring.

Pre-ignition may not be noticed if not severe. Severe pre-ignition results in severe pinging. The commonest cause of pre-ignition is a badly overheated engine.

When the engine won't stop when the ignition is shut off, the cause is often due to red hot carbon particles resting on heavy carbon deposit in a very hot engine.

ENGINE KICKBACK

If ignition is set too far advanced, spark may occur before top dead center when engine is cranked. The first (and only) explosion runs the engine backward. A kickback may jam the starter or break the starter drive housing.

BACKFIRE

Backfiring is a subdued explosion in the intake manifold. Causes are:

1. Lean mixture (often due to dirt or water in fuel).

2. Engine cold and choke too lean.
3. Leaky or sticking intake valve or weak or broken intake valve spring.
4. Leakage of current across distributor cap may cause backfire by enabling spark to occur in a cylinder which is on its intake stroke. Two mixed-up spark plug wires may also cause this trouble.
5. Popping back is same as backfire.

MUFFLER EXPLOSION

1. Late ignition timing.
2. Late valve timing.
3. Burnt exhaust valve(s).
4. Weak or broken exhaust valve spring(s).
5. Tight exhaust valve(s).
6. Intermittent open circuit in primary (ammeter needle swings further away from zero when generator is charging).
7. Intermittent short in primary (ammeter swings toward zero when generator is charging).
8. Short in coil or secondary coil wire.
9. If just a couple of explosions are heard and then no more for a time (even for days) the trouble may be due to a gradually failing condenser.

AFTER-BURNING

A subdued put-putting at the exhaust tail pipe may be due to leaky exhaust valves which permit the mixture to finish combustion in the muffler. If exhaust pipe or muffler is red hot, better let it cool, as there is some danger of setting the car on fire. Most likely to occur when mixture is lean.

FLAT SPOT

If an engine does not respond promptly when the throttle is opened quickly it (or the carburetor) is said to have a flat spot. This is usually caused by any of the following:

1. Accelerator pump piston (or diaphragm) leaks.
2. Accelerator pump valves leak.
3. Accelerator pump stroke too short.
4. Accelerator pump passages restricted.
5. Fuel volatility too low or too high.
6. Float level too low.
7. Fuel pump pressure too low.
8. The anti-percolating valve (on some carburetors) may open too soon when throttle is closed. If so, carburetor may have flat spot next time throttle is opened when engine is hot.
9. Fuel too hot due to hot engine and hot weather (see Vapor Lock).
10. If carburetor has a metering pin operated by throttle linkage and also a vacuum piston linked to the throttle to give a rich mixture at part throttle and moderate engine speed, a flat spot will be noted if the device fails to function properly because of stuck piston, vacuum leakage or restricted vacuum passages.
11. If carburetor has vacuum piston which provides richer mixture at part throttle and moderate engine speed by opening an additional passage or jet within carburetor, a flat spot will occur if fuel valves fail to work, or fuel passages are restricted, or if piston does not function because it is sticking, vacuum leakage or restricted vacuum passages.
12. Late ignition timing.

ENGINE FAILS TO REACH OPERATING TEMPERATURE

1. Defective thermostat.
2. Thermostat stuck open.
3. Thermostat removed from vehicle (during flushing cooling system and not replaced).
4. Defective temperature sending unit or dash unit.

ENGINE CONTINUES TO RUN AFTER
IGNITION IS TURNED OFF

This condition, known as "dieseling," "run on," or "after running," is caused by improper idle speed and/or high temperature. Idle speed and engine temperature are affected by:

Carburetor Adjustment: High idle speed will increase the tendency to diesel because of the inertia of the engine crankshaft and flywheel. Too low an idle speed, particularly with a lean mixture, will result in an increase in engine temperature, especially if the engine is allowed to idle for long periods of time.

Ignition Timing: Because advanced ignition timing causes a corresponding increase in idle speed and retarded timing reduces idle speed, ignition timing influences the tendency to diesel in the same manner as Carburetor Adjustment.

Fuel Mixture: Enriching the idle fuel mixture decreases the tendency to diesel by causing the engine to run cooler.

Fuel Content: High octane fuels tend to reduce dieseling. Increased fuel content of lead alkyl increases the tendency to diesel. Phosphates and nickel fuel additives help prevent dieseling.

Spark Plugs: Plugs of too high a heat range for the engine in question can cause dieseling.

Throttle Plates: If the throttle plates are not properly aligned in the carburetor bore, a resulting leanness in fuel mixture occurs, contributing to dieseling.

Electrical System: Normally, during dieseling, ignition is self-supplied by a "hot spot," self-igniting fuel, etc. However, there is a possibility of the vehicle's electrical system supplying the necessary ignition. When the ignition switch is turned off, a small amount of current can flow from the generator into the primary of the ignition coil through the generator tell-tale light. This is particularly true when the warning light bulb has been changed for one of increased wattage.

NOTE: "Run on" is more prevalent in an engine when the ignition is turned off before the engine is allowed to return to idle. Therefore, it can be reduced by letting the engine return to idle before shutting off the ignition. "Run on" incidence can be reduced on automatic transmission units by turning off the engine when in gear.

A certain amount of "run on" can be expected from any gasoline engine regardless of make, size or configuration. (Diesel engines operate on this principle.) However, if the above suggestions are correctly employed, "run on" will be reduced to an unnoticeable level.

ENGINE OVERHEATS: WATER COOLED

Water is used to cool the engine and air is used to cool the water. Anything which prevents this water-air system from working properly will cause overheating. Oil or grease in the water will reduce the ability of the water to absorb heat from the block and to transfer heat in the water to the radiator. There are six basic causes of overheating:

1. Water does not cool engine.
2. Air does not cool water.
3. Pre-ignition.
4. Pinging.
5. Excessive friction in engine or elsewhere in power transmitting units.
6. Excessive back pressure in exhaust system.

Water Too Hot

1. Slipping fan belt.
2. Not enough water in system.
3. Carburetor mixture too lean.
4. Clogged exhaust system.
5. Late ignition timing.
6. Centrifugal advance fails to advance spark as engine speed increases because weights stick or because of sticking elsewhere in mechanism.

7. Pre-ignition.
8. Detonation.
9. Water circulation impeded by installation of wrong cylinder head gasket.
10. Cylinder head gasket installed incorrectly, blocking off water holes.
11. Leaky cylinder head gasket permits exhaust gas to enter water. The gas bubbles interfere with the ability of the water to cool the engine.
12. Water circulation slowed down by rust, scale or dirt in water jackets.
13. Water distributing tube (when used) within cylinder block rusted out, dented or improperly installed so that not enough water reaches some cylinders, thus causing local overheating.
14. Local overheating at one cylinder (or more) due to heavy deposit of rust, scale or dirt in water jacket around cylinder or exhaust valve port.
15. Water circulation impeded by thermostat which fails to open fully or sticks closed.
16. Water temperature increased by thermostat which fails to open at correct temperature. Or the installation of a thermostat which opens at too high a temperature.
17. Any water hose which has rotted on inside, allowing loosened strips of rubber to impede water circulation.
18. The baffle in top tank may be bent in such a way as to interfere with free discharge of water from the hose.
19. Water passages in radiator are partially clogged with dirt, rust, corrosion or scale (mineral salts in hard water).
20. Exterior of radiator clogged with dirt, leaves or insects.
21. Rotting of water hose may weaken it so that pump suction causes it to collapse when engine is running fast, thus throttling the water flow.

22. If water pump seal leaks, air may be drawn into the water. Air bubbles in cooling water reduce the cooling ability of the water.
23. Water pump impeller loose on its shaft or impeller blades badly corroded.
24. Overheats due to alcohol type anti-freeze during mild weather.

WATER LEAKAGE

Cylinder Head

1. Loose attaching bolts.
2. Dirty, corroded or burred surface prevents tight fit.
3. Warped surface does not fit tight against gasket.
4. Cracked due to freezing or excessive heat.
5. On overhead valve head, exhaust valve seats may be cracked, allowing water to leak into cylinders and crankcase.

Cylinder Block

1. Dirty, corroded or burred surface prevents tight fit.
2. Warped surface does not fit tight against gasket.
3. Cracked due to freezing or excessive heat.
4. Excessive heat may crack exhaust valve seats, allowing water to leak into crankcase.
5. Block cracked due to use of cylinder head bolt which is too long.
6. Leaky expansion plugs or pipe plugs in water jacket.

Cylinder Head Gasket

1. Dirty, corroded or broken.
2. Loose because cylinder head bolts are loose.
3. Leaks because it cannot make tight contact between head and block.

Water Pump

1. Loose pump.
2. Faulty gasket.
3. Improper installation.
4. Warped pump body or dirty metal surfaces.
5. Hole or crack in pump body.
6. Worn seal.
7. Seal improperly installed.
8. Bent pump shaft.
9. Loose bearings or bushings or worn pump shaft.

Radiator

1. Leaks due to freezing or corrosion.
2. Strain due to improper attachment to car.
3. Fan striking radiator.
4. Drain plug or petcock leaks.
5. Radiator baffle bent so that water is directed into overflow pipe.
6. Clogged radiator causing water to pile up in upper tank which causes coolant to flow out overflow pipe.

Hose

1. Hose clamps loose.
2. Hose improperly installed.
3. Hose rotted through.

Heater: See that all heater connections are tight and that its radiator does not leak.

ENGINE OVERHEATS: AIR COOLED

These engines run at a higher operating temperature and depend on circulation of air across the cooling fins to keep temperature at a safe level. Over-heating can be caused by:

1. Broken fan belt.
2. Seized blower bearing.
3. Jammed or misadjusted damper doors.

4. Defective damper door thermostats.
5. Engine cooling fins clogged with leaves, dirt, etc.
6. Oil cooler fins clogged.
7. Lean carburetor mixture.
8. Incorrect ignition timing.
9. Pre-ignition.
10. Detonation.

ENGINE OIL LEAKAGE

NOTE: If engine is equipped with a positive crankcase vent valve, check the valve for proper operation before checking causes of leak. A clogged crankcase vent valve can build up pressure in the crankcase which will cause seals and gaskets to leak.

1. Oil pan drain plug loose or gasket missing.
2. Crack or hole in oil pan.
3. Oil pan gasket leaks due to: (a) loose screws; (b) damaged gasket; (c) improperly installed gasket; (d) bent oil pan flange.
4. Timing case cover gasket leaks due to: (a) loose screws; (b) damaged gasket; (c) improperly installed gasket; (d) bent cover flange; (e) leakage at engine support plate.
5. Front crankshaft oil seal leaks due to: (a) worn oil seal; (b) seal not properly installed; (c) rough surface on crankshaft, or fan pulley or damper; (d) damper or pulley loose; (e) seal or cover not centered on crankshaft; (f) oil return passage to crankcase clogged up (if provided).
6. Rear main bearing oil seal leaks due to: (a) worn oil seal; (b) improper oil seal installation; (c) worn rear main bearing; (d) rough crankshaft surface.
7. Oil return passage to crankcase clogged.
8. Expansion plug in block at rear of camshaft leaks due to poor fit, careless installation, or corrosion.

9. Leakage at any external piping.
10. Plugs at ends of oil passages in cylinder block leak.
11. Oil filter leaks.
12. Leakage at distributor housing.
13. Valve cover leaks due to loose screws, defective gasket, improperly installed gasket or bent cover flange.
14. Rocker arm cover or push rod cover leaks because of loose screws, defective gasket, improper gasket installation or bent cover flange.
15. Pipe connections loose on oil gauge or oil filter lines.
16. Loose oil pump or faulty gasket (if pump is on outside of block).
17. Clogged breather and/or crankcase ventilating discharge pipe, permits increase in pressure within engine, thus causing oil to be forced out past any oil seals or gaskets.
18. If oil pressure relief valve is mounted on outside of block, leakage may occur if unit is loose or its gaskets defective.

HIGH OIL CONSUMPTION

1. External oil leaks.
2. Leaky piston rings due to wear.
3. Leaky piston rings due to sticking caused by gummy deposit. Try to free up with suitable solvent poured in fuel tank. Blue smoke at tail pipe indicates badly leaking rings.
4. Worn pistons and cylinders.
5. Cylinder block distorted by tightening cylinder head bolts unevenly.
6. Excessive clearance between intake valve stems and guides allows oil mist to be sucked into cylinders.
7. Punctured vacuum pump diaphragm permits oil from crankcase to be sucked into intake manifold.

8. Worn main or rod bearings allow excessive leakage from bearings. Result is cylinder walls are flooded with oil.
9. Oil pressure too high due to faulty action of oil pressure relief valve, or clogged relief passage.
10. If pressure lubricated, loose piston pins may permit excessive leakage to cylinder walls.
11. Grade of oil used is too light. A poor quality oil may become far too thin when engine is hot. Hard driving on hot days will also consume more oil.
12. Clogged crankcase ventilator system.

OIL PRESSURE RELIEF VALVE LEAKS

1. Relief valve needs tighter adjustment.
2. Relief valve spring weak or broken.
3. Valve seat worn or distorted.
4. Plunger type valve face worn.
5. Plunger type valve stuck open.
6. Ball type valve damaged.
7. Pump discharge pipe or passages leak.

ENGINE OIL DILUTION

1. Oil contains foam caused by presence of water in oil. Water may be due to condensation within crankcase or to a leaky cylinder head gasket.
2. Extreme dilution of oil by fuel may add enough liquid to oil to mislead. In extreme cases, oil level may increase. Dilution is greatest when frequent stops are made in cold weather.

NO OIL PRESSURE

1. Oil pressure gauge defective.
2. Pipe to oil pressure gauge stopped up.

3. Not enough oil in crankcase.
4. Oil pump inoperative.
5. Oil pressure relief valve stuck open.
6. Oil passages on discharge side of pump stopped up.
7. Oil screen or passages on intake side of pump stopped up.

LOW OIL PRESSURE

1. Oil pressure gauge inaccurate.
2. Pipe to pressure gauge restricted.
3. Oil too thin due to dilution, poor quality, or too light a grade used.
4. Oil pressure relief valve adjustment too light.
5. Relief valve spring weak.
6. Oil pump gears worn.
7. Oil pump cover worn.
8. Oil pump body or cover loose.
9. Oil pump gasket damaged, improperly installed or too thick.
10. Air leak in oil intake pipe (if oil level is low).
11. Air leak in top of floating screen (if used).
12. Oil intake pipe or screen clogged with water, sludge, gummy oil, dirt or ice.
13. Oil leak in discharge pipe.
14. Loose connections in oil lines.
15. Worn main, rod or camshaft bearings.

HIGH OIL PRESSURE

1. Oil pressure gauge defective.
2. Oil too heavy.
3. Oil pressure relief valve adjustment too heavy.
4. Relief valve spring too stiff.
5. Oil pressure relief passage clogged.
6. Plunger type relief valve stuck by gummy oil or plunger is too tight a fit.

7. Main oil passages on pressure side of pump clogged.

ENGINE NOISES

Loose Main Bearing

A loose main bearing is indicated by a powerful but dull thud or knock when the engine is pulling. If all main bearings are loose a noticeable clatter will be audible.

The thud occurs regularly every other revolution. The knock can be confirmed by shorting spark plugs on cylinders adjacent to the bearing. Knock will disappear or be less when plugs are shorted. This test should be made at a fast idle equivalent to 15 mph in high gear. If bearing is not quite loose enough to produce a knock by itself, the bearing may knock if oil is too thin or if there is no oil at the bearing.

Loose Flywheel

A thud or click which is usually irregular. To test, idle the engine at about 20 mph and shut off the ignition. If thud is heard, the flywheel may be loose.

Loose Rod Bearing

A metallic knock which is usually loudest at about 30 mph with throttle closed. Knock can be reduced or even eliminated by shorting spark plug. If bearing is not loose enough to produce a knock by itself, the bearing may knock if oil is too thin or if there is no oil at the bearing.

Piston Pin

Piston pin, piston and connecting rod noises are difficult to tell apart.

A loose piston pin causes a sharp double knock which is usually heard when engine is idling. Severity of knock should increase when spark plug to this cylinder is short-circuited. However, on some engines the knock becomes more noticeable at 25 to 35 mph on the road.

Piston pin rubs against cylinder wall, caused by lock screw being loose or snap ring broken.

Piston & Rings

1. Excessive clearance between pistons and cylinders (piston slap).
2. Out-of-round or tapered bores.
3. Top piston ring strikes ridge at top of cylinder bore.
4. Carbon deposit on top of piston strikes cylinder head.
5. Piston rubs against cylinder head gasket.
6. Broken piston ring.
7. Excessive side clearance of ring in groove.
8. Worn or broken piston ring lands.
9. Broken piston.

Valves

1. Valve click due to too much tappet clearance, hydraulic tappet not working properly, warped valve, sticking valve, binding rocker arm.
2. Insufficient oil to valve mechanism, especially overhead valves.
3. Worn or scored parts anywhere in valve mechanism.
4. Broken valve springs.
5. Weak valve springs.
6. Cocked valve springs.
7. Excessive tappet guide clearance.
8. Lower end of tappet scored, chipped, rough, worn or broken.
9. Very rough surface on cams.
10. Excessive valve stem-to-guide clearance.
11. Valve face not concentric with valve stem.
12. Valve seat face not concentric with valve stem.
13. Valve covers on overhead valve engines tightened excessively will amplify normal valve noise.

Hydraulic Lifters

The malfunctioning of a hydraulic valve lifter is almost always accompanied by a clicking or tapping noise. More or less hydraulic lifter noise may be expected when the engine is cold but if lifters are functioning properly the noise should disappear when the engine warms up.

If all or nearly all lifters are noisy, they may be stuck because of dirty or gummy oil.

If all lifters are noisy, oil pressure to them may be inadequate. Foaming oil may also cause this trouble. If oil foams there will be bubbles on the oil level dipstick. Foaming may be caused by water in the oil or by too high an oil level or by a very low oil level.

If the hydraulic plungers require an initial adjustment, they will be noisy if this adjustment is incorrect.

If one lifter is noisy the cause may be:
1. Plunger too tight in lifter body.
2. Weak or broken plunger spring.
3. Ball valve leaks.
4. Plunger worn.
5. Lock ring (if any) improperly installed or missing.
6. Lack of oil pressure to this plunger.

If ball valve leaks, clean plunger in special solvent such as acetone and reinstall. Too often, plungers are condemned as faulty when all they need is a thorough cleaning.

Gum and dirty oil are the most common causes of hydraulic valve lifter trouble. Engine oil must be free of dirt. Select a standard brand of engine oil and use no other. Mixing up one standard brand with another may cause gummy oil or sticking plungers. Do not use any special oils unless recommended by the car manufacturer and change oil filter or element at recommended intervals.

Timing Gears

1. Gears loose on hubs or shafts.
2. Gears misaligned.
3. Excessive gear backlash.

4. Eccentric gear, usually due to high key.
5. Teeth meshed too tight (new oversize gear).
6. Too much end play in camshaft or crankshaft.
7. Front crankshaft bearing clearance excessive.
8. Chipped tooth usually on camshaft gear.

Timing Chain

1. Chain loose due to wear.
2. Sprocket teeth worn.
3. Sprockets loose on hubs or shafts.
4. Sprockets misaligned.
5. Front camshaft bearing clearance excessive.
6. Front main bearing clearance excessive.
7. Loose vibration damper or drive pulley.

Loose Engine Mountings

Occasional thud with car in operation. Most likely to be noticed at the moment the throttle is opened or closed.

Excessive Crankshaft End Play

A rather sharp rap which occurs at idling speed but may be heard at higher speeds also. The noise should disappear when clutch is disengaged.

Water Pump

1. Water pump shaft pulley loose.
2. Impeller loose on shaft.
3. Too much end play in pump shaft.
4. Too much clearance between shaft and bearings.
5. Impeller blades rubbing against pump housing.
6. Impeller pin sheared off or impeller broken.
7. Rough bearing.
8. Pump seal too hard.

Fan Belt

1. Belt worn or burned.
2. Wrong belt. Does not fit pulley grooves properly.
3. Belt too tight. Squeaks.

4. Belt or pulley dirty or sticky with gummy oil.
5. Pulley bent, cracked or broken.
6. Belt pulleys misaligned.
7. Belt loose; squeaks when engine is accelerated.

Fan

1. Fan blades bent.
2. Fan blades loose on hub.
3. Fan out of balance when made.
4. Fan blades strike radiator.
5. Fan shaft end play excessive.
6. Fan shaft loose on its bearings.
7. Defective fan bearings.
8. Bearings need lubrication.

Engine Vibration

1. Unequal compression in cylinders.
2. Missing at high speed.
3. Unbalanced fan or loose fan blade.
4. Incorrect adjustment of engine mounts, or damaged mounts.
5. Loose engine mounts.
6. Engine support loose on frame or cylinder block.
7. Unbalanced or sprung crankshaft.
8. Excessive engine friction due to tight pistons, etc.
9. Defective vibration damper.

Fuel Pump Noise

Diagnosis of fuel pumps suspected as noisy requires that some form of sounding device be used. Judgment by ear alone is not sufficient, otherwise a fuel pump may be needlessly replaced in attempting to correct noise contributed by some other component. Use of a stethoscope, a long screwdriver, or a sounding rod is recommended to locate the area or component causing the noise. The sounding rod can easily be made from a length of copper tubing ¼ to ⅜ inch in diameter.

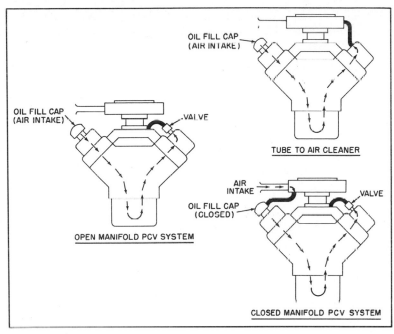

OIL FILL CAP
(AIR INTAKE)

VALVE

TUBE TO AIR CLEANER

AIR
INTAKE

OIL FILL CAP
(CLOSED)

VALVE

OIL FILL CAP
(AIR INTAKE)

VALVE

OPEN MANIFOLD PCV SYSTEM

CLOSED MANIFOLD PCV SYSTEM

Fig. 1   Various PCV systems

If the noise has been isolated to the fuel pump, remove the pump and run the engine with the fuel remaining in the carburetor bowl. If the noise level does not change, the source of the noise is elsewhere and the original fuel pump should be reinstalled. On models using a fuel pump push rod, check for excessive wear and/or galling of the push rod.

▶ EMISSION CONTROL SYSTEM TROUBLES

CRANKCASE VENTILATION SYSTEM

Fresh air is circulated through the engine crankcase and drawn into the intake manifold, carrying crankcase vapors with it, Fig. 1. This air flow is controlled by a spring loaded ventilation valve which is closed during high vacuum periods and opens to provide maximum ventilation as manifold vacuum drops off.

Because the hoses vent directly into the intake manifold, any malfunction in the system will have a direct effect on the carburetor mixture calibration. For this reason, the valve and hoses must be kept clear and all connections must be air tight.

The system should be checked and the valve cleaned or replaced at every tune-up and any time there is an engine idle complaint.

SYSTEM TEST

A quick check of the system can be made by pulling the end of the valve out of the valve cover and, with the engine idling, placing a finger over the end of the valve to block the air flow. A vacuum should be felt and the engine speed should drop approximately 50 rpm if the system is satisfactory. If there is no change in engine speed a clogged system is indicated. To isolate the problem, remove the valve from the hose. If the ventilator hoses and carburetor passages are clear, a strong vacuum will be felt and the engine idle will change drastically or the engine will stall when the end of the hose is uncovered. If this occurs, the trouble is in the valve. If the engine continues to idle approximately as it did before the hose was uncovered, the hoses or carburetor passages are blocked.

Regulator Valve Test

1. Install a regulator valve known to be good in the crankcase ventilation system.
2. Start engine and compare engine idle condition to the prior idle condition.
3. If the loping or rough idle condition remains when the good regulator valve is installed, the crankcase ventilation system is not at fault. Further engine component diagnosis will have to be made to find the cause of the malfunction.
4. If the idle condition proves satisfactory, replace the regulator valve and clean hoses, fittings, etc.

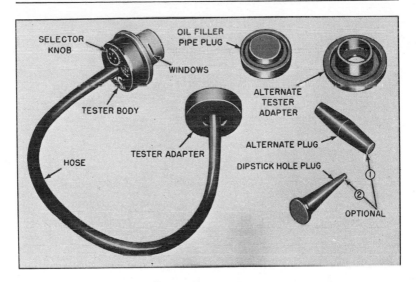

Fig. 2   AC positive crankcase ventilation system tester

Air Intake Test

This test uses the AC positive crankcase ventilation tester, Fig. 2, which is operated by the engine vacuum through the oil filler opening.

1. With engine at normal operating temperature, remove oil filler cap and dipstick.
2. Connect one end of the hose to the tester body and connect the other end of the hose to the tester adapter.
3. Use the dipstick hole plug to plug the opening in the dipstick tube.
4. Insert the tester adapter in the filler cap opening and turn the selector knob to No. 2 (Fig. 2).
5. If the vehicle has a system with the tube from the air cleaner going into the oil filler cap, disconnect the tube at the filler cap and plug the tube.
6. Start engine and let it idle.
7. With plugs secure and tube free of kinks, hold

tester body upright and note color in the tester windows. Following lists the various colors and probable cause or related condition of the system.

GREEN: System operating properly.

GREEN & YELLOW

1. Regulator valve or system partially plugged.
2. Slight kink in tester hose.
3. Slight engine blow-by.
4. Plugs from kit or engine vacuum lines are not properly sealed.
5. Tester knob improperly set.

YELLOW

1. Regulator valve or system partially plugged.
2. Tester hose kinked or blocked.
3. Blow-by at maximum capacity of regulator valve.
4. Plugs from kit or engine vacuum lines are not properly sealed.
5. Tester knob improperly set.

YELLOW & RED

1. Regulator valve or system partially or fully plugged.
2. More engine blow-by than regulator valve can handle.
3. Vent hose plugged or collapsed.

RED

1. Regulator valve or system fully plugged or stuck.
2. Vent hose plugged or collapsed.
3. Extreme blow-by.

AIR INJECTION SYSTEM

The design of the system is such that certain carburetor and distributor recalibrations are necessary for best performance. In addition, before performing any diagnosis involving the system, it must be determined that other engine components are functioning properly. To do this, the main control or backfire suppressor valve vacuum sensing hose and air supply hose *must be disconnected at the intake manifold.*

For best results and most efficient operation, the emission control system hoses, tubes, oil separator screen, fittings and carburetor spacer should be cleaned. The emission control valve must be replaced every 12,000 miles. Also the air pump filter element must be replaced every 12,000 miles.

If engine components not part of the emission control system are functioning properly, use the following diagnosis guide to isolate emission control system malfunctions.

Excessive Backfiring in Exhaust System

Check for damaged, plugged, disconnected or leaking backfire suppressor valve or vacuum sensing hose. A defective backfire suppressor valve results in an insufficient air delivery to the intake manifold or air delivery not timed to engine requirement.

Excessive Hesitation on Acceleration

If there is excessive hesitation on acceleration after sudden throttle closure above 20 mph, look for intake vacuum leak at the backfire suppressor valve, vacuum hose or air outlet hose to intake manifold. Also check for a defective or malfunctioning backfire suppressor valve.

Air Supply Hoses

If air supply hose or hoses are baked or burned, look for a defect in the exhaust system or check valve.

Engine Surges at All Speeds

Backfire suppressor valve defective or stuck open. Also check for improperly adjusted carburetor—idle speed, idle speed mixture, automatic choke, etc.

Noisy Pump Belt

Drive belt improperly adjusted. Seized or failing air pump. Misaligned or defective pulleys.

Rough Engine Idle

Improper carburetor adjustment. Improper ignition timing. Intake manifold leak at backfire suppressor valve vacuum hose or air inlet hose. Backfire suppressor valve defective or stuck open.

▶ ELECTRICAL TROUBLES

NOTE: Ignition troubles are included in the *Engine Troubles* section under the various operating difficulties these troubles could cause.

BATTERY REQUIRES FREQUENT RECHARGING

Insufficient Current Flow to Battery

1. Defective generator or alternator.
2. Incorrect voltage regulator setting.
3. Regulator contacts oxidized or burned.
4. Sulphated battery.
5. Corroded battery terminals.
6. Regulator not grounded.
7. Loose connections or grounds in lighting or ignition circuits.
8. Slipping fan belt.
9. Blown regulator fuse.
10. Wrong size generator drive pulley.
11. Shorted or open alternator rectifiers.
12. Grounded stator windings in alternator.

Excessive Starting Load Causing Abnormal
Current Flow from Battery

1. Frequent use of starting motor.
2. Excessive use of starting motor due to difficulty in starting.

3. Faulty starting motor.
4. Excessive engine friction due to tight pistons, etc., or heavy engine oil.

Excessive Lighting Load

1. Car operation confined largely to night driving.
2. Tail and stop light wires reversed.
3. Stop light switch inoperative (closed at all times).
4. Unnecessary use of head lamps while parking.
5. Ground or short in lighting circuit.

Abnormal Accessory Load

1. Radio.
2. Heater.
3. Windshield defroster.
4. Cigar lighter.
5. Spotlights.

Internal Discharge of Battery

1. Plates badly sulphated.
2. Cell leak due to cracked jar or sealing compound.
3. Water level not maintained at proper height.
4. Plate separators ineffective.
5. Exterior of battery covered with corrosion and acid-soaked dirt which forms a path to ground for current.

Miscellaneous

Radio suppressor connected to generator or regulator field terminal.

STARTER WON'T ROTATE OR ROTATES SLOWLY

If lights become dim or go out when the starter switch is closed, the battery may be too weak to operate the starter. In this case, the engine may be started by pushing the car.

NOTE: Some cannot be started by pushing because these transmissions have no rear oil pump to drive the engine through the transmission. In such cases, a fully charged battery should be installed or a "jumper" circuit should be used from another charged battery.

Cars equipped with alternators cannot be push started if the battery is completely dead because alternators retain no residual magnetism.

Due to Starter Circuit

1. Low battery. Lights grow very dim or go out when starter switch is closed.
2. Connections loose, dirty, corroded or broken at battery terminals, starter switch terminal, battery ground strap.
3. Short circuit across starter terminal.

Due to Starter Switch

1. Starter pedal (if any) stuck.
2. Starter switch stuck.
3. Pedal linkage fails to close starter switch (older cars).
4. Defective solenoid.
5. Neutral safety switch on cars with automatic transmissions out of adjustment or defective.
6. Starter switch makes poor contact due to dirt, corrosion, bent parts, weak contact spring.
7. Starter switch fails to close circuit because of sticking or broken contact parts.

Due to Armature & Field Circuits

1. Armature windings burned out, shorted, grounded or open-circuited.
2. Short circuit in armature winding or brush pigtail lead.

3. Broken wire in armature winding or brush pigtail lead.
4. Loose, dirty or corroded connections in armature circuit, including ground.
5. Field coils burned out, shorted or grounded.
6. Broken wire in field winding or broken lead.
7. Loose, dirty or corroded connections in field circuit.

Due to Commutator & Brushes

1. Brush pigtail leads loose or broken.
2. Starter brushes cracked crosswire (prevents flow of current).
3. Arm type brush holder sticks.
4. Brush sticks in sliding brush holder.
5. Bent brush holder misaligns brush and causes poor contact.
6. Starter brushes badly worn.
7. Brush leads shorted or have loose, dirty, corroded or broken connections.
8. Poor brush contact due to weak or broken springs.
9. Brushes coated with oil.
10. High mica between commutator segments prevents brush contact.
11. Commutator bars loose and/or solder melted.
12. Commutator dirty, corroded or burned.

Due to Engine Resistance

1. Piston sticking to cylinders in overheated engine.
2. Pistons stuck to cylinders because of gummy oil.
3. Pistons binding in cylinders because of corrosion after long lay-up.
4. Jammed generator armature.
5. Combustion chamber full of water.
6. Solid ice in water pump.
7. Broken part in engine causes jamming.
8. Excessive engine friction, due to cold weather and too heavy oil.

Due to Improper Engine Repairs

1. New rings too tight.
2. New pistons too tight.
3. Main or rod bearings too tight.
4. New camshaft bearings too tight.

Due to Armature Binding

1. Loose field poles.
2. Armature shaft frozen in bearings.
3. Loose end plates.
4. Windings thrown out of armature slots.
5. Armature locked magnetically to field poles because of loose bearings or worn or bent armature shaft.
6. Bendix spring retaining screws loose (jammed against housing).
7. Cracked or distorted drive housing.
8. Starter misaligned.
9. Starter jams because of burred teeth on drive pinion or flywheel gear.
10. Starter pinion (sliding gear type) jams because of incorrect endwise clearance.

STARTER SPINS BUT WON'T ENGAGE FLYWHEEL GEAR

Bendix Type

1. Bendix pinion stuck on shaft due to dirty or gummy shaft or bent shaft.
2. Bendix spring broken.
3. Bendix spring bolt broken.
4. Pinion housing cracked.
5. Drive key sheared.
6. Pinion teeth broken off.
7. Starter ring gear has several teeth missing.
8. Armature shaft broken.

Sliding Gear Type

1. Weak or broken meshing spring.
2. Fault in sliding gear linkage.
3. Fault in solenoid.
4. Over-running clutch worn out or lubricant caked or gummy.
5. Drive key sheared.
6. Pinion teeth broken off.
7. Flywheel ring gear has several teeth missing.
8. Armature shaft broken, dirty or dry.
9. Wrong starter pinion clearance.

STARTER PINION JAMMED INTO FLYWHEEL GEAR FLYWHEEL GEAR

1. Burred teeth on pinion or ring gear.
2. Misalignment of starter or armature shaft.
3. If engine kicks back when being started, Bendix pinion may jam. Loosen starter to free pinion.

STARTER PINION DISENGAGES SLOWLY

Bendix Type

The most probable cause is a dirty Bendix drive shaft. Or the pinion may bind on its shaft due to a bent shaft or too tight a fit between pinion and splines.

When a Bendix Folo-Thru starter drive stays in mesh too long it is probably due to a sticking release pin which is designed to be released by centrifugal force at a certain engine rpm. In such an instance the drive should be replaced.

Sliding Gear Type

1. Pinion binds on its shaft due to too tight a fit or due to bent or burred shaft.
2. Pinion shaft sticky or dirty.
3. Sliding gear operating linkage sticking or binding.
4. Solenoid does not operate properly.

STARTER PINION WON'T RELEASE

Bendix Folo-Thru Drive

Failure to disengage would most probably be caused by a stuck release pin which is designed to be released by centrifugal force at a given engine rpm. If such is the case, replace the drive unit.

Sliding Gear Type

If solenoid operated, the solenoid may be defective. If pedal operated, the shift linkage may be binding or sticking. May also be caused by a defective starter switch on cars with key-starter switch or by improper starter pinion clearance.

STARTER NOISE

1. Loose pole pieces rubbing against armature.
2. Gear noise due to defective teeth.
3. Flywheel ring gear untrue.
4. Starter drive housing loose on flywheel housing.
5. Starter loose on drive housing.
6. Commutator end plate loose.
7. Armature shaft bent.
8. Worn armature shaft, bearings or bushings.
9. Drive pinion shaft bent.
10. Worn drive pinion shaft, bearings or bushings.
11. Misalignment caused by dirt or burrs on mating surfaces.

GENERATOR DOES NOT CHARGE

1. Fan belt broken or slips badly.
2. Belt pulley slips on armature shaft.
3. Cutout relay fails to close.
4. Armature won't rotate because of seized bearing, etc.
5. External wiring from generator to starter switch

terminal short-circuited or circuit is open because of detached wire or very dirty or corroded connection.

6. Voltage regulator inoperative.
7. Open circuit or short circuit in armature or field windings.
8. Brushes stuck.
9. Brushes coated with oil.
10. Brush lead connections dirty or disconnected.
11. Improperly seated brushes.
12. Weak brush springs.
13. Very dirty commutator.
14. Burned or corroded commutator.
15. Commutator bars short-circuited.
16. High mica on commutator.
17. Solder melted at commutator bar connections.

GENERATOR NOISE

1. Generator loose on engine.
2. Generator end plates loose.
3. Armature shaft bent.
4. Armature shaft worn.
5. Bushing or bearing worn or needs lubrication.
6. Armature shaft end play excessive.
7. Generator pulley loose on its shaft.
8. Generator or pulley misaligned.
9. Bent, cracked or broken pulley.
10. Generator fan rubs on generator.

GENERATOR BRUSH NOISE

1. High mica between commutator bars.
2. Sprung armature shaft.
3. Rough, dirty or glazed commutator.
4. Worn or loose brushes.
5. Commutator out of round.

6. Brushes not seating properly.
7. Too little or too much brush spring tension.

ALTERNATORS

Alternator Fails to Charge

1. Drive belt loose.
2. Brushes sticking.
3. Open charging circuit.
4. Open in stator winding circuit.
5. Faulty soldered connections at output terminal stud.
6. Rectifiers open circuited.

Low Unsteady Charging Rate

1. Drive belt loose.
2. High resistance at battery terminal posts.
3. Loose connections.
4. Poor ground between engine and body ground wire.
5. Resistance in charging circuit.
6. Open stator windings.

Low Output

1. Grounded stator.
2. Shorted rectifier.
3. Voltage regulator faulty.

Excessive Charging Rate

1. Voltage regulator faulty.
2. Open circuited rectifier.

Noisy Alternator

1. Misaligned belt or pulley, or loose pulley.
2. Shorted rectifier.
3. Worn bearings.
4. Rotor shaft sprung.

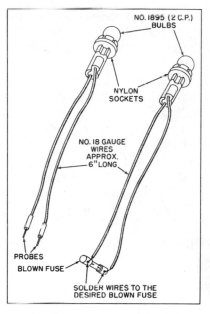

Fig. 3   Test lamp for locating shorts

Regulator Points Oxidized

1. Poor ground connections.
2. Improper voltage regulator air gap setting.
3. Shorted field in alternator.
4. Voltage regulator setting too high.

Burned Points or Coil Windings in Regulator

1. Voltage regulator setting too high.

Voltage Regulator Points Stuck

1. Poor ground connections between alternator and regulator.

LOCATING ELECTRICAL SHORTS WITH TEST LAMP

Due to the complexity of locating electrical short circuits where several circuits are protected by the same fuse, fabricate a test lamp from the material shown in the accompanying illustration, Fig. 3. By substituting the test lamp for the blown fuse the short circuit can be isolated.

When the test lamp is inserted into the fuse panel, the bulb will light and continue to glow until the short circuit is removed. Determining which circuit is at fault can be accomplished by disconnecting the affected circuits one at a time until the test lamp goes out. Then trace the circuit to find the cause of the short (wire contacting sharp sheet metal edges, wire pinched between two metal objects, etc.).

For circuits that are not connected to the fuse panel but are protected by an in-line fuse cartridge, use a test lamp having two needle point probes in place of the blown fuse. Insert one probe through the insulation and into the wire on each side of the blown in-line fuse and follow the same testing procedure outlined above.

FUSIBLE LINKS

Some cars starting with 1965 models have fusible links located between the battery and the lower ends of the main supply wires. These links are the weakest point in the electrical supply system for the entire car and, as such, will act as a fuse for every wiring harness in the car. Every electrical accessory is still protected by a fuse or circuit breaker, of course, but fusible links have been added to protect the wiring harnesses *before* the fuses.

In the past, if a wire became grounded in the portion between the battery and the fuse block, a long section of the wire would burn out, making replacement of a complete wiring harness necessary. Now, with the fusible links, a short or ground in any unfused wire will cause only a short link to burn out. Because of its location, possibility of a fire, such as was sometimes caused by a burned-out wiring harness, is very remote.

A fusible link is simply a short section of wire that is several sizes smaller in gauge than the wire in the circuit which it protects. If a short or ground occurs the fusible link will

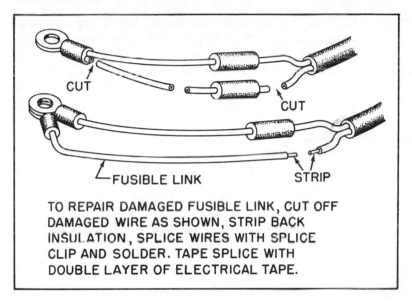

TO REPAIR DAMAGED FUSIBLE LINK, CUT OFF
DAMAGED WIRE AS SHOWN, STRIP BACK
INSULATION, SPLICE WIRES WITH SPLICE
CLIP AND SOLDER. TAPE SPLICE WITH
DOUBLE LAYER OF ELECTRICAL TAPE.

Fig. 4   Repairing fusible links

melt before the insulation is damaged elsewhere in the circuit. Replace burned-out fusible link as directed in the illustration, Fig. 4.

LIGHTS FLICKER

Circuit Breaker Vibrates

When the circuit breaker vibrates and causes lights to
flicker it indicates a short in one of the lighting circuits,
which may be traced as follows:

    1. Pull switch successively to each lighting position.
If circuit breaker vibrates in all positions except
"off" the trouble should be found in the tail lamp
and license lamp circuit, or instrument, map light,
or clock light circuits.

    2. If circuit breaker vibrates in parking lamp position
only, look for a short in the parking lamp circuit.

3. If circuit breaker vibrates in headlamp position only, inspect headlamp wiring circuit and lamp assemblies. If both filaments in headlamps burn at the same time, check dimmer switch.

LAMPS FAIL TO BURN

1. Burned out bulb.
2. An open circuit in wiring.
3. A defective switch.
4. Burned out fuse.

LIGHTS FLARE UP WHEN ENGINE IS SPEEDED UP

This condition is caused by high voltage in the electrical system due to one or more of the following:
1. Electrolyte in battery low or weak.
2. High resistance in circuit between generator and battery due to loose or dirty connections.
3. Poor ground between generator and engine.
4. Voltage regulator adjusted too high.
5. Voltage regulator inoperative.
6. Ground or short in generator field circuit.

STOP LIGHT TROUBLES

1. If only one stop light fails to burn, check lamp bulb, socket and wiring.
2. If both stop lights fail to burn also check stop light switch and fuse.
3. If stop light burns when brake pedal is released, check stop light switch, brake pedal clearance and for dragging brakes.
4. If compensating port in brake master cylinder is plugged by foreign material, or is covered by the piston primary cup when brake pedal is released,

high pressure will be maintained in hydraulic system and stop light switch will remain closed.

TURN SIGNAL TROUBLES

1. If signals arc inoperative on both turns, look for a blown fuse or a defective flasher.
2. If stop lights burn, the fuse and rear signal lamp bulbs are okay.
3. An inoperative right signal light may be caused by a burned out bulb at the right indicator or a right signal lamp. The opposite applies for an inoperative left signal light.
4. If bulbs are okay, look for an open circuit or defective switch.
5. If indicator light on dash burns steady when lever is placed in a turn position, check for burned out bulb in park or stop light. If park and stop light bulbs arc okay, check for faulty flasher.
6. If indicator light on dash does not burn when lever is in a turn position, check for burned out bulb or a faulty flasher.
7. If switch fails to cancel after completion of turn, remove steering wheel and check for worn or broken mechanism.

ELECTRIC CLOCKS

If clock does not run, check for blown "clock" fuse. If fuse is blown check for short in wiring. If fuse is not blown check for open circuit.

With an electric clock, the most frequent cause of clock fuse blowing is low voltage at the clock which will prevent a complete wind and allow clock contacts to remain closed. This may be caused by any of the following: discharged battery, corrosion on contact surface of battery terminals, loose connections at battery terminals, at junction block, at fuse clips, or at terminal connection of clock. Therefore, if in reconnecting battery or clock it is noted that the clock is not ticking, always check for blown fuse, or examine the circuits at the points indicated above to determine and correct the cause.

HAZARD WARNING FLASHER TROUBLES

To make a quick check of the system pull Hazard Warning switch to ON position. The rear turn signal bulbs should flash as well as the front turn signal bulbs, turn signal indicator bulbs and pilot bulb. All lights will burn continuously when the brake pedal is depressed; this is normal.

Pilot Bulb Fails to Flash

Check for burned out bulb and loose or defective ground wire. Replace bulb, repair ground wire or tighten ground wire screw. If this does not correct the condition, replace flasher switch and harness assembly. Then repeat quick check procedure.

All Bulbs Fail to Flash

1. Check for loose harness connections at Hazard Warning connectors and secure connectors if necessary.
2. Check for a burned out tail and stop light fuse and replace if necessary.
3. Check for a defective Hazard Warning flasher or switch. This may be done by removing the flasher and installing a known good flasher.
4. Pull switch to ON position. If flasher does not operate properly, replace flasher switch and harness assembly, installing old flasher. If system still does not operate properly, install new flasher along with new switch.

Some Bulbs Fail to Flash While Others are Operative

1. Turn ON ignition switch and turn OFF Hazard Warning switch.

2. Place turn signal lever first to right and then to left turn position. If turn signal circuits operate properly, the Hazard Warning switch and harness assembly should be replaced.
3. If the same bulbs fail to flash, the cause is most likely a burned out bulb. In the case of turn signal indicator bulbs, a loose or defective ground wire can also cause this condition. Repair as necessary.

NOTE: If any turn signal bulb fails to flash when the turn signal circuit is actuated, the reduced current in the circuit will cause the remaining signals on that side of the car to burn steadily. If the Hazard Warning flasher is energized, however, all turn signal bulbs and indicator bulbs will flash except those that have a circuit defect. They will flash at a constant rate unless the battery is completely run down. This is because the Hazard Warning flasher overrides the turn signal circuit flasher.

4. If the condition is still not resolved, disconnect the Hazard Warning connectors and again check the operation of the turn signal circuits. If the affected bulbs now flash, replace flasher switch and harness assembly.
5. If the condition is still not resolved, look for defects in the connectors to the affected bulb.
6. Repeat quick check test.

▶ CLUTCH TROUBLES

Clutch Drags

Clutch drag means that when the clutch pedal is depressed fully the clutch disc is not completely released. In consequence it does not come to rest but continues to rotate, being dragged around by the rotation of the engine. Clutch dragging causes clashing of gears, especially when shifting from neutral to low or reverse.

1. Pedal cannot disengage clutch because of excessive free pedal travel. Pedal linkage should be adjusted so that the pedal shank is about 1" from the under side of the toe-board.
2. Worn clutch linkage.
3. Release levers need adjustment.
4. Clutch disc warped out of true.
5. High spot on clutch facing.
6. Broken or loose facings.
7. Loose rivet in facing.
8. Clutch disc hub binds on splined clutch shaft due to bent shaft, tight fit, burred splines or splines covered with gummy oil or dirt.
9. Clutch disc wobbles because of broken springs in hub.
10. Clutch disc hub out of true.
11. Clutch shaft bent.
12. Clutch shaft out of true because of worn bearings.
13. Transmission is not in alignment with flywheel housing.
14. Clutch pressure plate warped, thus throwing release levers out of adjustment.
15. Flange of clutch cover not in alignment with flywheel because of loose attaching screws, bent flange, dirt between flange and flywheel.
16. Grease on clutch facings.
17. Engine misaligned due to deteriorated or broken engine mounts.
18. Loose flywheel housing-to-engine attaching bolts.
19. Release fork pivot worn.

Clutch Slips

The clutch disc slips whenever the clutch pressure plate fails to hold it tight against the face of the flywheel. If clutch slippage is severe, the engine speed will rise above normal on full throttle in high gear. Slight but continuous slippage may go unnoticed until the clutch facings are ruined by excessive temperature caused by friction.

In a very high percentage of cases, clutch slippage is due to less than zero clearance between the shank of the pedal and the toe-board because of failure to have the pedal adjusted in time. The consequence is worn and burned clutch facings. Before the clutch starts slipping, the normal wear of the facings causes a gradual reduction in clutch pedal free play. When there is no free play of the pedal the clutch starts slipping.

Other causes of clutch slippage are:
1. Driving with foot resting on pedal.
2. Binding or sticking of pedal or its linkage.
3. Binding or sticking of clutch disc hub on clutch shaft.
4. Binding of release levers.
5. Release bearing sleeve sticks.
6. Weak or broken clutch pressure springs.
7. Worn clutch facings.
8. Facings covered with grease or oil.
9. Facings burned.
10. Release levers improperly adjusted.
11. Pressure plate sticks.

Clutch Grabs

A clutch is said to grab when it engages too abruptly. The usual causes are:
1. Loss of tension in cushioning plates in the rim of the steel clutch disc. These plates cause the clutch facings to bulge outward slightly. The resulting springy action of the facings aids in producing a smooth, gentle clutch engagement.
2. Use of wrong type of clutch facing.
3. Grease or oil on facings.
4. Clutch springs too stiff.
5. Momentary binding in clutch linkage while clutch is being engaged.
6. Exposed rivet heads due to excessively worn facings or loose rivets.

Clutch Chatters

If a clutch chatters while it is being engaged, the trouble is caused by rapid gripping and slipping. The usual causes are:

1. Somewhat sticky clutch friction surfaces due to gummy lubricant.
2. Clutch friction surfaces damp or wet.
3. Weak clutch springs.
4. Slight binding in clutch linkage during engagement.
5. Slight binding of pressure plate during engagement.
6. Loose engine mounts.

Clutch Pedal Pulsates

Clutch pedal pulsation has often been termed a nervous pedal. When a slight pressure is applied on the pedal, with the engine running, the pedal will vibrate or bounce with every revolution of the engine. As the pressure on the pedal is increased, the pulsation will cease.

1. Loose or improperly adjusted engine mounts.
2. Collar on clutch release sleeve does not run true due to a bent clutch shaft, or the clutch shaft misaligned because of misalignment between crankshaft and transmission.
3. Clutch release levers not adjusted to uniform height.

Clutch Rattles

This condition will occur when the engine is idling with transmission in neutral.

1. Excessive clearance at pressure plate driving lugs.
2. Anti-rattle springs or retractor springs on release levers (or release bearing) weak, broken or disconnected.
3. Looseness in clutch pedal operating linkage.
4. Loose flywheel.

Noise When Pedal Is Depressed

1. Clutch release bearing worn, dirty, damaged, broken or inadequately lubricated.
2. Clutch shaft bearing or bushing in crankshaft worn, damaged, broken or inadequately lubricated.
3. Clutch shaft rear bearing at front end of transmission, worn, dirty or lacks lubricant.

Noise When Pedal Is Released

1. Misalignment of transmission with engine causing slight wobble of clutch disc hub—noticeable with engine idling or at low road speed.
2. Disc hub loose fit on splined clutch shaft.
3. Disc damper springs weak or broken.
4. No pedal play.
5. Weak or broken pedal return spring.
6. Weak or broken release sleeve spring.
7. Clutch linkage sticks.
8. Clutch pedal sticks.
9. Clutch release sleeve sticks.
10. Clutch release fork binds.
11. Bad clutch release bearing.
12. Loose flywheel.

BEARING NOISE

Clutch Release Bearing:—With engine idling, there is a high-pitched rubbing noise when foot rests on clutch pedal.

Clutch Pilot Bearing:—Fairly high-pitched noise when clutch pedal is fully depressed with engine idling.

▶ RAMBLER "E-STICK" TROUBLES

NOTE: *In addition to the troubles listed below, the clutch is subject to the same troubles, such as Chatter, Grabbing, etc., as the conventional type clutch.*

Excessive Slip

1. Low servo oil pressure.
2. Release lever improperly adjusted or release fork not installed on release bearing guide pins.
3. Low engine oil level.
4. Air valve solenoid inoperative or leaking excessively.
5. Check valve orifice blocked in servo.
6. Diaphragm push rod stuck in valve and diaphgram assembly.
7. Diaphragm vent plugged.

Excessive Creep

1. Retractor spring too light or broken.
2. Servo oil pressure too high.
3. Broken retractor straps.

No Clutch Release

1. Bent or damaged diaphragm cover.
2. Vacuum lines leaking.
3. Control valve stuck in valve body.
4. Actuating switch not operating properly.
5. Actuating switch cam out of adjustment.
6. Faulty wiring circuit to air valve solenoid.
7. Air valve solenoid not functioning.
8. Servo piston binding in its bore.
9. Diaphragm push rod sticking.
10. Air vent in servo body plugged.
11. Vacuum diaphragm leaking.

Engine Overspeeds on Clutch Engagement

1. Clutch release lever out of adjustment.
2. Servo piston binding in its bore.
3. Servo body vent hole plugged.
4. Oil regulator valve not seating.
5. Servo check valve sticking on shaft.
6. Check valve orifice in servo restricted.

No Clutch Engagement

1. Actuating switch not operating properly.
2. Actuating switch cam out of adjustment.
3. Faulty wiring circuit to air valve solenoid.
4. Air valve solenoid not functioning.
5. Lube valve stuck closed.
6. Servo piston binding in its bore.
7. Broken spring in dump diaphragm.
8. Oil pressure regulator valve stuck open.
9. Low engine oil level.

▶ THREE SPEED TRANSMISSION

GENERAL MOTORS TRANSMISSION WITH SECOND SPEED GEAR LOCATED AT REAR OF MAINSHAFT

Slips Out of High and/or 2nd Gear

1. Transmission mounting bolts loose.
2. Control rods interfere with engine mounts or clutch release lever.
3. Control linkage does not work freely.
4. Gear does not fully engage.
5. Damaged mainshaft pilot bearing.
6. Clutch gear bearing retainer broken or loose.
7. Dirt between transmission case and clutch housing (front mounted), or between transmission case and differential carrier (rear mounted).
8. Misalignment of transmission.
9. Worn or broken synchronizer assembly.
10. Weak springs in transmission cover.

Slips Out of Low and/or Reverse

1. First and/or reverse gears damaged from operating at part engagement.
2. Improperly mated splines on inside of first and reverse gear and/or external splines on 2nd and 3rd synchronizer sleeve.

3. Improperly adjusted linkage.
4. Weak spring in transmission cover.

Noisy in All Gears

1. Not enough lubricant.
2. Worn countergear bearings.
3. Worn or damaged clutch gear and countershaft drive gear.
4. Damaged clutch gear or mainshaft ball bearings.
5. Damaged speedometer gears.

Noisy in High Gear

1. Damaged clutch gear bearing.
2. Damaged mainshaft bearing.
3. Damaged speedometer gears.

Noisy in Neutral with Engine Running

1. Damaged clutch gear bearing.
2. Damaged mainshaft pilot bearing roller.

Noisy in All Reduction Gears

1. Not enough lubricant.
2. Worn or damaged clutch gear or countershaft drive gear.

Noisy in Second Only

1. Damaged or worn 2nd speed gears.
2. Worn or damaged countergear rear bearings.

Noisy in Low and Reverse Only

1. Worn or damaged 1st and reverse sliding gear.
2. Damaged or worn low and reverse countergear.

Noisy in Reverse Only

1. Worn or damaged reverse idler.
2. Worn reverse idler bushings.
3. Damaged or worn reverse countergear.

Excessive Backlash in Second Only

1. Second gear thrust washer worn.
2. Mainshaft rear bearing improperly installed in case.
3. Worn countergear rear bearing.

Excessive Backlash in Reduction Gears

1. Worn countergear bushings.
2. Excessive end play in countergear.

Leaks Lubricant

1. Too much lube in transmission.
2. Loose or broken clutch gear bearing retainer.
3. Clutch gear bearing retainer damaged.
4. Cover loose or gasket damaged.
5. Operating shaft seal leaks.
6. Idler shaft expansion plugs loose.
7. Countershaft loose in case.
8. Lack of sealant on bolts.

ALL TRANSMISSIONS WITH LOW-REVERSE GEAR LOCATED AT REAR OF MAINSHAFT

Noises

When diagnosing transmission noise note the gear position in which the noise occurs. Noise present in all gear positions may be due to worn or damaged constant mesh gears or bearings. Noise present in only one gear can usually be traced to the particular gear involved. Other causes of noise are as follows:

1. Misalignment due to loose mounting bolts.
2. Clutch housing misalignment.
3. Dirt or metal chips in lubricant.
4. Not enough lube in transmission.
5. Improper lubricant.

Hard Shifting

1. Clutch linkage out of adjustment.
2. Linkage improperly adjusted.
3. Linkage binding due to bent, worn or broken parts.
4. Gearshift tube binding due to misaligned steering gear housing.
5. Improper lube in transmission.
6. Damaged synchronizer assembly.

Jumps Out of Gear

1. Improper shift procedure.
2. Linkage parts worn, bent, broken or out of adjustment.
3. Excessive end play caused by wear in shift forks, sliding gear fork grooves, thrust washers, mainshaft and countershaft bearings, or clutch pilot bushing.
4. Misalignment or excessive clearance between sliding gear and mainshaft.
5. Damaged synchronizer.

Leakage

1. Overfilled tranmission or using a lube that foams or expands while car is in operation.
2. Loose gearshift housing capscrews.
3. Damaged gaskets.
4. Transmission vent plugged.
5. Extension housing rear seal leaks.

▶ 4-SPEED TRANS. TROUBLES CORVAIR & 1961–63 TEMPEST

Slips Out of Gear

1. Transmission loose on differential carrier.
2. Control linkage binds or does not fully engage.
3. Damaged or missing mainshaft pilot bearings.

4. Clutch gear bearing retainer loose or broken.
5. Dirt between transmission case and differential carrier.
6. Worn or damaged synchronizer.
7. Weak detent spring(s).

Noisy in All Gears

1. Insufficient lubricant.
2. Worn countergear bearings.
3. Worn or damaged clutch gear and countergear.
4. Damaged clutch gear bearing or mainshaft rear bearing.

Noisy in High Gear

1. Damaged clutch gear bearing.
2. Damaged mainshaft bearing.

Noisy in Neutral

1. Damaged clutch gear bearing.
2. Damaged mainshaft pilot roller bearings.

Noisy in All Reduction Gears

1. Insufficient lubricant.
2. Worn or damaged clutch gear or countergear.

Noisy in 2nd Only

1. Damaged or worn 2nd speed gears.
2. Worn or damaged countergear bearings.

Noisy in Low & Reverse

1. Worn or damaged low and reverse sliding gear.
2. Damaged or worn low and reverse countergear.

Noisy in Reverse Only

1. Worn or damaged reverse idler gear.
2. Worn reverse idler gear bushings.
3. Worn or damaged countergear reverse teeth.

Excessive Backlash in All Reduction Gears

1. Worn countergear bushings.
2. Excessive end play in countergear.

Leaks Lubricant

1. Too much lubricant in transmission.
2. Loose or broken clutch gear bearing cover.
3. Clutch gear bearing retainer gasket.
4. Cover loose or gasket damaged.
5. Shifter shaft seal leaks.
6. Countershaft loose in case.

ALL CARS OTHER THAN CORVAIR & 1961–63 TEMPEST

Noisy in All Speeds

1. Incorrect lubricant level.
2. Incorrect type lubricant.
3. Countergear bearings worn or damaged.
4. Countergear worn or damaged.
5. Clutch gear bearing worn or damaged.
6. Mainshaft bearing worn or damaged.
7. Clutch gear worn or damaged.
8. Transmission misaligned or loose.

Noisy in 1st Speed

1. First gear worn or damaged.
2. Countergear worn or damaged.
3. Countergear bearings worn or damaged.
4. Synchronizers worn or broken.
5. Countershaft worn or damaged.

Noisy in 2nd Speed

1. Second gear worn or damaged.
2. Countergear worn or damaged.
3. Countergear bearings worn or damaged.

4. Synchronizers worn or broken.
5. Countershaft worn or damaged.

Noisy in 3rd Speed

1. Third gear worn or damaged.
2. Countergear worn or damaged.
3. Countergear bearings worn or damaged.
4. Synchronizers worn or broken.
5. Countershaft worn or damaged.

Noisy in 4th Speed

1. Clutch shaft bearing worn or damaged.
2. Mainshaft bearing worn or damaged.
3. Synchronizers worn or broken.

Noisy in Reverse

1. Reverse idler gear or shaft worn or damaged.
2. Reverse sliding gear worn or damaged.
3. Shift linkage out of adjustment.
4. Shift linkage bent or damaged.
5. Shift linkage parts loose.
6. Shift levers, shafts or forks worn.

Shifts Hard

1. Clutch pedal free travel incorrect.
2. Clutch parts worn or damaged.
3. Shift linkage out of adjustment.
4. Shift linkage bent or damaged.
5. Shift linkage parts loose.
6. Shift levers, shafts or forks worn.
7. Lubricant type incorrect.
8. Lubricant level incorrect.

Jumps Out of Gear

1. Shift linkage out of adjustment.
2. Shift linkage bent or damaged.
3. Shift linkage parts loose.

4. Shift levers, shafts or forks worn.
5. Shift cover loose or gasket damaged.
6. Transmission misaligned or loose.
7. Synchronizers worn or broken.
8. Clutch gear bearing retainer broken.
9. Clutch gear bearing worn or damaged.
10. Clutch pilot bearing worn or broken.
11. Mainshaft and/or pilot worn or damaged.
12. Mainshaft bearing worn or damaged.

Leaks Lubricant

1. Lubricant level incorrect.
2. Lubricant type incorrect.
3. Vent plugged.
4. Clutch gear bearing retainer or gasket loose.
5. Clutch gear bearing retainer broken.
6. Shift cover loose or gasket damaged.
7. Shifter shaft seals leaking.
8. Shift cover bolts not sealed.
9. Countershaft loose in case bore.

▶ OVERDRIVE TROUBLES

Diagnosis

Figs. 5 to 8 illustrate the overdrive circuit diagrams in use. Since overdrive troubles may originate not only in the mechanical operation of the unit but also in the electrical circuit which controls that unit, always check the control system before disassembling the overdrive. If the trouble is not found after a thorough inspection of the control system, then the transmission and overdrive should be removed for examination. If the overdrive operation is unsatisfactory, look for:

1. Blown fuse in governor-solenoid circuit.
2. Loose terminals on any of the connecting wires.
3. Incorrect terminal location of connecting wires.
4. Circuits grounded by water, dirt or deformation.

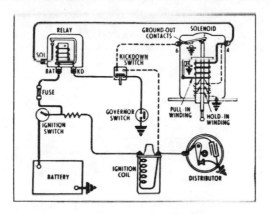

Fig. 5   Overdrive circuit diagram with relay

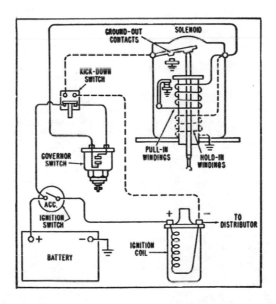

Fig. 6   Overdrive circuit diagram without relay. Beginning with 1964

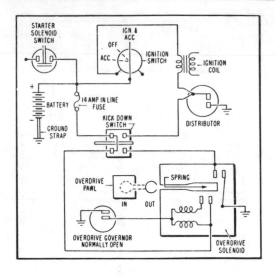

Fig. 7   Overdrive circuit diagram without relay. 1958–63

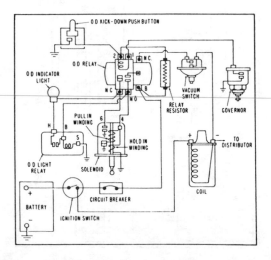

Fig. 8   Rambler twin stick overdrive circuit diagram. Beginning with 1964

5. Defective solenoid points.
6. Insufficient travel or unsatisfactory contacts in kickdown switch.
7. Excessive end play in governor shaft.
8. Improper adjustment of governor control springs.
9. Burned governor contact points.
10. Damage to governor cap and contacts.
11. Absence of rubber cover to exclude water and dirt.
12. Insufficient travel of shift rod (adjust control cable).

MECHANICAL TROUBLES

Overdrive Won't Drive Unless Locked Up Manually

1. Occasionally the unit may not drive the car forward in direct drive unless locked up by pulling the dash control. This may be caused by one or more broken rollers in the roller clutch the remedy for which is to replace the entire set of rollers.
2. This condition may also be caused by sticking of the roller retainer upon the cam. This retainer must move freely to push the rollers into engaging position under the pressure of the two actuating springs.
3. Sometimes this condition is due to slight indentations, worn in the cam faces by the rollers spinning, remedied by replacing the cam.

Overdrive Does Not Engage or Lock-Up Does Not Release

1. Dash control improperly connected.
2. Transmission and overdrive improperly aligned.
3. Kickdown switch improperly adjusted.
4. Improper installation of solenoid.
5. Improper positioning of blocker ring.
6. Broken or slipping governor drive pinion.
7. Too much end play in mainshaft.

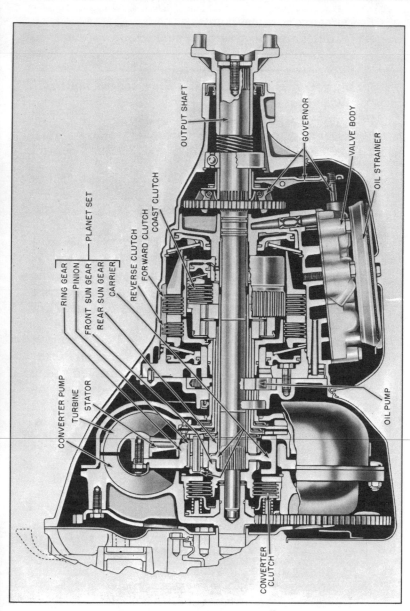

Fig. 9 Cutaway of Dual Path transmission

Overdrive Engages with Severe Jolt or Noise

Insufficient blocker ring friction may cause the ring to lose its grip on the hub of the sun gear control plate.

Free-Wheels At Speeds Over 30 MPH

If cam roller retainer spring tension is weak the unit will free-wheel at all times.

▶ AUTOMATIC TRANSMISSION TROUBLES

▶ BUICK SPECIAL DUAL-PATH DRIVE, Fig. 9

With linkage properly adjusted and engine warmed up, make a road test and observe general performance of transmission and check for abnormal noises. Accelerate from a stop with accelerator depressed just to detent. Upshift should occur smoothly between 40 and 45 mph. If upshift occurs at speeds other than those specified, refer to text below for possible causes.

Upshifts Below Normal Speed

1. Governor valve not adjusted properly or sticking.
2. Shift valve or shift regulator valve sticking.
3. Throttle valve pressure too low. Could be worn or broken spring or sticking valve.

Upshifts Above Normal Speed

1. Governor valve not adjusted properly or sticking.
2. Shift valve or shift regulator sticking.
3. Throttle valve pressure too high valve sticking.

Slow, Lagging Upshift

1. Converter pressure regulator valve sticking. This results in a slower lowering of converter pressure and a slow engagement of converter clutch.

Harsh Upshift

1. Converter pressure regulator valve sticking and creating a low converter pressure at all times. This

results in a harsh, fast engagement of the converter clutch.

Car Won't Move or Slips in Reverse

1. Coast clutch slipping, burned out or not engaged.
2. Reverse clutch slipping, burned out or not engaged.
3. Front overrunning clutch slipping.
4. Forward clutch locked up or not releasing.

Car Won't Move or Slips on Take-Off in Drive or Low

1. Forward clutch slipping, burned out or not engaged.

Car Won't Upshift in Drive Range

1. Throttle valve stuck in high pressure position or throttle valve linkage may be binding holding throttle valve open.
2. Converter clutch slipping, burned out or not engaged.
3. Converter pressure regulator valve stuck keeping converter pressure high at all times.
4. Governor valve stuck in "Off" position or improperly adjusted.
5. Shift valve stuck in "Off" position or shift regulator valve stuck.

Car Coasts on Deceleration in Low

1. Coast clutch slipping, burned out or not engaged.

Car Locks Up When it Upshifts in Drive Range

1. Coast clutch locked up or not releasing.
2. Rear overrunning clutch locked up.

Car Backs Up in Neutral

1. Reverse clutch locked up or not releasing.

Car Pulls Forward in Neutral

1. Forward clutch locked up or not releasing.
2. Converter clutch locked up or not releasing.

Car Labors on Take-Off or Stalls

1. Converter clutch locked up or not releasing.

Car Slips on Take-Off in Drive or Low

1. Front overrunning clutch slipping.

Engine Labors When Approaching Cruising Speed

1. Front overrunning clutch locked up.

Car Won't Move in Drive

1. Rear overrunning clutch slipping.

Car Labors on Take-Off in Drive—Cruises Normally but Will Not Downshift

1. Governor valve stuck in "Open" position.
2. Shift valve stuck in converter clutch "On" position.

Upshifts Early but Will Not Downshift

1. Throttle valve stuck in "Off" position.

Upshifts Only at High Speed

1. Throttle pressure regulator valve stuck causing throttle pressure to be too high.
2. Throttle detent valve stuck wide open.

Upshifts Early except at Wide Open Throttle

1. Shift regulator stuck.

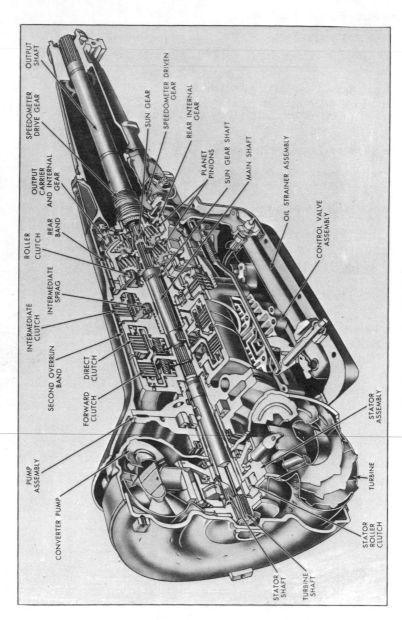

Fig. 10   Cutaway of 1965–67 transmission

▶ BUICK SUPER TURBINE "400" & TURBO HYDRA-MATIC "400," Fig. 10

Oil Pressure High or Low

1. Vacuum line or fittings clogged or leaking.
2. Vacuum modulator.
3. Modulator valve.
4. Pressure regulator.
5. Oil pump.
6. Governor.

No Drive in Drive Range

1. Low oil level (check for leaks).
2. Manual control linkage not adjusted properly.
3. Low oil pressure. Check for blocked strainer, defective pressure regulator, pump assembly or pump drive gear. See that tangs have not been damaged by converter.
4. Check control valve assembly to see if manual valve has been disconnected from manual lever pin.
5. Forward clutch may be stuck or damaged. Check pump feed circuits to forward clutch, including clutch drum ball check.
6. Sprag or roller clutch assembled incorrectly.

1-2 Shift at Full Throttle Only

1. Detent switch may be sticking or defective.
2. Detent solenoid may be stuck open, loose or have leaking gasket.
3. Control valve assembly may be leaking, damaged or incorrectly installed.

1st Speed Only—No. 1-2 Shift

1. Governor valve may be sticking.
2. Driven gear in governor assembly loose, worn or damaged.

3. The 1-2 shift valve in control valve assembly stuck closed. Check governor feed channels for blocks, leaks, and position. Also check control valve body gaskets for leaks and damage.
4. Intermediate clutch plug in case may be leaking or blown out.
5. Check for porosity between channels and for blocked governor feed channels in case.
6. Check intermediate clutch for proper operation.

No 2-3 Shift—1st & 2nd Only

1. Detent solenoid may be stuck open.
2. Detent switch may not be properly adjusted.
3. Control valve assembly may be stuck, leaking, damaged, or incorrectly installed.
4. Check direct clutch case center support for broken, leaking or missing oil rings.
5. Check clutch piston seals and piston ball check in clutch assembly.

Moves Forward in Neutral

1. Manual control linkage improperly adjusted.
2. Forward clutch does not release.

No Drive in Reverse or Slips in Reverse

1. Check oil level.
2. Manual control linkage improperly adjusted.
3. Vacuum modulator assembly may be defective.
4. Vacuum modulator valve sticking.
5. Strainer may be restricted or leaking at intake.
6. Regulator or boost valve in pump assembly may be sticking.
7. Control valve assembly may be stuck, leaking or damaged.
8. Rear servo and accumulator may have damaged or missing servo piston seal ring.
9. Reverse band burned out or damaged. Determine that apply pin or anchor pins engage properly.

10. Direct clutch may be damaged or may have stuck ball check in piston.
11. Forward clutch does not release.
12. Low-reverse ball check missing from case.

Slips in All Ranges & on Starts

1. Check oil level.
2. Vacuum modulator defective.
3. Modulator valve sticking.
4. Strainer assembly plugged or leaking at neck.
5. Pump assembly regulator or boost valve sticking.
6. Leaks from damaged gaskets or cross leaks from porosity of case
7. Forward and direct clutches burned.

Slips 1-2 Shift

1. Incorrect oil level.
2. Vacuum modulator valve sticking.
3. Vacuum modulator defective.
4. Pump pressure regulator valve defective.
5. Porosity between channels in case.
6. Control valve assembly.
7. Pump-to-case gasket may be mispositioned.
8. Intermediate clutch plug in case may be missing or leaking excessively.
9. Intermediate clutch piston seal missing or damaged.
10. Intermediate clutch plates burned.
11. Front or rear accumulator oil ring may be damaged.

Slips 2-3 Shift

1. Items 1 through 6 under Slips 1-2 Shift will also cause 2-3 shift slips.
2. Direct clutch plates burned.
3. Oil seal rings on direct clutch may be damaged per-

mitting excessive leaking between tower and bushing.

Rough 1-2 Shift

1. Modulator valve sticking.
2. Modulator assembly defective.
3. Pump pressure regulator or boost valve stuck or inoperative.
4. Control valve assembly loosened from case, damaged or mounted with wrong gaskets.
5. Intermediate clutch ball missing or not sealing.
6. Porosity between channels in case.
7. Rear servo accumulator assembly may have oil rings damaged, stuck piston, broken or missing spring or damaged bore.

Rough 2-3 Shift

1. Items 1, 2 and 3 under Rough 1-2 Shift will also cause rough 2-3 shift.
2. Front servo accumulator spring broken or missing. Accumulator piston may be sticking.

No Engine Braking in Second Speed

1. Front servo or accumulator oil rings may be leaking.
2. Front band may be broken or burned out.
3. Front band not engaged on anchor pin and/or servo pin.

No Engine Braking in Low Range

1. Low-reverse check ball may be missing from control valve assembly.
2. Rear servo may have damaged oil seal ring, bore or piston; leaking, apply pressure.
3. Rear band broken, burned out or not engaged on anchor pins or servo pin.

No Part Throttle Downshifts

1. Vacuum modulator assembly.
2. Modulator valve.
3. Regulator valve train.
4. Control valve assembly has stuck 3-2 valve or broken spring.

No Detent Downshifts

1. Detent switch needs fuse, connections tightened or adjustment.
2. Detent solenoid may be inoperative.
3. Detent valve train in control valve assembly malfunctioning.

Low or High Shift Points

1. Oil pressure. Check vacuum modulator assembly, vacuum line connections, modulator valve, and pressure regulator valve train.
2. Governor may have sticking valve or feed holes that are leaking, plugged or damaged.
3. Detent solenoid may be stuck open or loose.
4. Control valve assembly. Check detent, 3-2, and 1-2 shift valve trains, and check spacer plate gaskets for positioning.
5. Check case for porosity, missing or leaking intermediate plug.

Won't Hold in Park

1. Manual control linkage improperly adjusted.
2. Internal linkage defective; check for chamfer on actuator rod sleeve.
3. Parking pawl broken or inoperative.

Excessive Creep at Idle

NOTE: Transmissions having the variable pitch stator.
1. High idle speed.
2. Stator switch inoperative or defective.

3. Stator solenoid defective.
4. Pump may have stator valve train stuck.
5. Pump lead wires disconnected or grounded out.
6. Pump feed circuit to stator may be restricted or blocked.
7. Converter out check valve may be broken or stuck.
8. Turbine shaft may have defective oil seal ring.
9. Stator orifice plug in case may be blocked.
10. Converter assembly defective.

Poor Performance—¾ Throttle

NOTE: Transmissions having the variable pitch stator.
1. Stator and detent switch inoperative.
2. Items 3 through 10 above will also cause poor performance at ¾ throttle.

Noisy Transmission

1. Pump noises caused by high or low oil level.
2. Cavitation due to plugged strainer, porosity in intake circuit or water in oil.
3. Pump gears may be damaged.
4. Gear noise in low gear of Drive Range-transmission grounded to body.
5. Defective planetary gear set.
6. Clutch noises during application can be worn or burned clutch plates.

▶ GM FRONT WHEEL DRIVE TURBO HYDRA-MATIC, Fig. 11

No Drive in "D" Range

1. Low oil level. Check for external leaks or vacuum modulator diaphragm leaking.
2. Manual linkage maladjusted. Correct alignment in manual lever shift quadrant.
3. Low oil pressure.

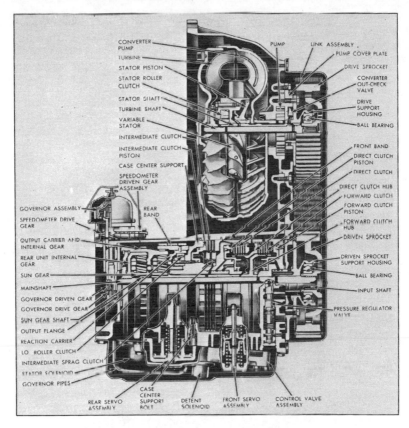

Fig. 11   Cutaway of Front Drive Turbo Hydra-Matic

4. Oil strainer O-ring seal missing or damaged, neck weld leaking, strainer blocked.
5. Oil pump pressure regulator stuck or inoperative. Pump drive gear tangs damaged by converter.
6. Case porosity in intake bore.
7. Control valve. Manual valve disconnected from manual lever pin. (Other shift lever positions would also be affected.)
8. Forward clutch does not apply. Piston cracked;

seals missing or damaged. These defects can be checked by removing the valve body and applying air pressure to the drive cavity in the case valve body face. Missing, damaged or worn oil rings on driven support housing can also cause the forward clutch not to apply. Clutch plates burned.

9. Roller clutch inoperative. Rollers worn, damaged springs, or damaged races. May be checked by placing selector lever in "L" range.

No Drive in "R" or Slips in Reverse

1. Low oil level.
2. Manual linkage.
3. Oil pressure. Vacuum modulator defective, modulator valve sticking. Restricted strainer, leak at intake pipe or O-ring seal. Pressure regulator or boost valve sticking.
4. Control valve body gaskets leaking or damaged (other malfunctions may also be indicated). Low-reverse check ball missing from case (this will cause no overrun braking in low range). The 2-3 valve train stuck open (this will also cause 1-3 upshifts in drive range). Reverse feed passage not drilled; also check case passages. Apply air to reverse passage in case valve body face.
5. Rear servo and accumulator. Servo piston seal ring broken or missing. Apply air pressure to drilled hole in intermediate clutch passage of case valve body face to check for piston operation and excessive leakage. Band apply pin too short (this may also cause no overrun braking or slip in overrun braking in low range).
6. Rear band burned, loose lining, apply pin or anchor pin not engaged; band broken.
7. Direct clutch outer seal damaged or missing. Clutch plates burned (may be caused by stuck ball check in piston).

8. Forward clutch does not release (will also cause drive in neutral range).

Drive in Neutral

1. Manual linkage maladjusted.
2. Forward clutch does not release (this condition will also cause no reverse).

1st Speed Only—No 1-2 Upshift

1. Governor valve sticking; driven gear loose, damaged or worn. If driven gear shows signs of wear or damage, check output flange drive gear for nicks or rough finish.
2. Control valve. The 1-2 shift valve train stuck closed. Dirt, chips or damaged valve in 1-2 shift valve train. Governor feed channels blocked or leaking; pipes out of position. Valve body gaskets leaking or damaged. Case porosity between oil channels. Governor feed passage blocked.
3. Intermediate clutch. Case center support oil rings missing, broken or defective. Clutch piston seals missing, improperly assembled, cut or damaged. Apply air to intermediate clutch passage located in case valve body face to check for these defects.

1-2 Shift Obtained Only at Full Throttle

1. Detent switch sticking or defective.
2. Detent solenoid loose, gasket leaking, sticks open, electrical wire pinched between cover and casting.
3. Control valve body gasket leaking or damaged. Detent valve train stuck.

1st & 2nd Speeds Only No 2-3 Shift

1. Detent solenoid stuck open (the 2-3 shift would occur at very high speeds) may be diagnosed as no 2-3 shift.
2. Detent switch sticking or defective.
3. Control valve body. The 2-3 valve train stuck with

dirt or foreign material. Valve body gaskets leaking or damaged.

4. Direct clutch. Case center support oil rings missing or broken. Clutch piston seals missing, improperly assembled, cut or damaged; piston ball check stuck or missing. Apply air to direct clutch passage in case valve body face to check these conditions.

Slips in All Ranges

1. Oil level incorrect.
2. Low oil pressure. Vacuum modulator defective or valve sticking. Oil strainer plugged or leaks at neck; O-ring (case to strainer) missing or damaged. Pressure regulator or boost valve sticking.
3. Case cross channel leaks; porosity.
4. Forward, intermediate and direct clutches slipping. Clutch plates burned. Always look for a primary defect that would cause clutch plates to burn (missing feed holes, seals and oil rings, etc., are primary defects).
5. Roller clutch rollers worn; springs or cage damaged, and worn or damaged races (operates normally in low and reverse ranges).

Slips 1-2 Shift

1. Oil level incorrect.
2. Low oil pressure. Look for defective vacuum modulator or valve sticking. Pump pressure regulator valve stuck.
3. Front servo accumulator piston cracked or porous, oil ring damaged or missing.
4. Control valve. The 1-2 accumulator valve train (may cause a slip-bump shift). Porous valve body or case valve body face.
5. Rear servo accumulator oil ring missing or damaged; case bore damaged; piston cracked or damaged.
6. Case porous between oil passages.

7. Intermediate clutch lip seals missing, cut or damaged. Apply air pressure to intermediate clutch passage in case valve body face to check. Clutch plates burned. Case center support leaks in feed circuits (oil rings damaged or grooves damaged) or excessive leak between tower and bushing.

Rough 1-2 Shift

1. Oil pressure. Check vacuum modulator for loose fittings, restrictions in line; defective vacuum modulator. Modulator valve stuck. Pressure regulator boost valve stuck.
2. Control valve. 1-2 accumulator valve train; valve body-to-case bolts loose; gaskets inverted, off location, or damaged.
3. Case. Intermediate clutch passage check ball missing or not seating. Case porous between channels.
4. Rear servo accumulator piston stuck. Apply air pressure to 1-2 accumulator passage in case valve body face (you should hear the servo piston move). Broken or missing spring; bore scored or damaged.

Slips 2-3 Shift

1. Oil level high or low.
2. Low oil pressure. Modulator defective or valve sticking. Pump pressure regulator valve or boost valve sticking.
3. Control valve. Accumulator piston pin leak at valve body end.
4. Direct clutch piston seals leaking. Case center support oil seal rings damaged or excessive leak between tower and bushing. Apply air to direct clutch passage, center support is defective.

Rough 2-3 Shift

1. Oil pressure high. Vacuum modulator defective or valve sticking. Pump pressure regulator valve or boost valve stuck or inoperative.

   2. Front servo accumulator spring missing or broken; accumulator piston stuck.

Shifts Occur at Too High or Too Low Car Speed

1. Oil pressure. Vacuum modulator defective or valve sticking. Leak in vacuum line (engine to transmission). Vacuum modulator line fitting on carburetor blocked. Pump pressure regulator valve or boost valve train stuck.
2. Governor valve stuck or sticking. Feed holes restricted or leaking; pipes damaged or mispositioned.
3. Detent solenoid stuck open or loose on valve body (will cause late shifts).
4. Control valve. Detent valve train sticking; 3-2 valve train sticking; 1-2 shift valve stuck; 1-2 detent valve sticking open (will probably cause early 2-3 shift).
5. Spacer plate gaskets inverted or mispositioned; orifice holes missing or blocked; check balls missing or mislocated.
6. Case porous in channels or foreign material blocking channels.

No Detent Downshift

1. Detent switch mispositioned or electrical connections loose.
2. Solenoid defective or electrical connections loose.
3. Control valve detent valve train stuck.

No Engine Braking—Super Range 2nd Speed

1. Front servo or accumulator piston rings broken or missing. Case or valve body bores worn oversize, causing excessive leakage.
2. Front band worn or burned (check for cause); band end lugs broken or damaged; band lugs not engaged on anchor pins or servo apply pin (check for cause).

No Engine Braking—Low Range 1st Speed

1. Control valve low-reverse check ball missing from case.
2. Rear servo oil ring damaged or missing; piston damaged or porous, causing a leak in apply pressure.
3. Rear band lining worn or burned (check for cause); band end lugs broken; band ends not engaged on anchor pin or servo apply pin. These items will also cause slip in reverse or no reverse.

Will Not Hold Car in Park Position

1. Manual linkage maladjusted (external).
2. Parking brake lever and actuator rod assembly defective (check for proper actuator spring action). Parking pawl broken or inoperative.

Poor Performance or Rough Idle

1. Stator switch defective or maladjusted.
2. Stator solenoid defective or wire ground to solenoid housing; electrical connection loose; stator valve train stuck (located in valve body); oil feed circuit to stator restricted or block (check feed hole in stator shaft); converter-out check valve broken or missing (reed valve located in cover plate under drive support housing).
3. Turbine shaft converter return passage not drilled; oil seal rings broken, worn or missing.
4. Case porous in feed circuit channels or foreign material blocking feed circuit.
5. Converter assembly defective.

Transmission Noise

1. Pump noise. Oil level high or low; water in oil, driving gear assembled upside down; driving or driven gear teeth damaged.

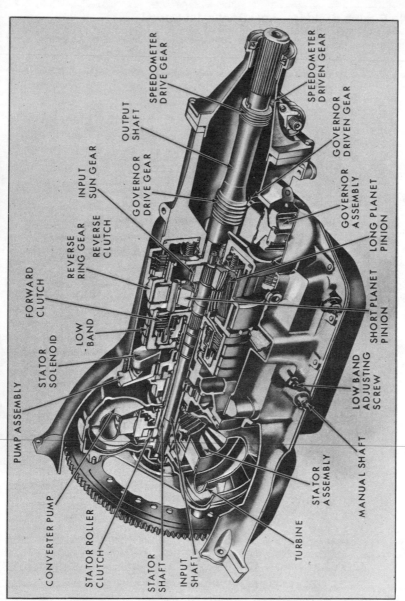

SPEEDOMETER DRIVE GEAR

SPEEDOMETER DRIVEN GEAR

OUTPUT SHAFT

INPUT SUN GEAR

GOVERNOR DRIVEN GEAR

GOVERNOR DRIVE GEAR

GOVERNOR ASSEMBLY

REVERSE RING GEAR

REVERSE CLUTCH

LONG PLANET PINION

FORWARD CLUTCH

LOW BAND

SHORT PLANET PINION

STATOR SOLENOID

LOW BAND ADJUSTING SCREW

PUMP ASSEMBLY

MANUAL SHAFT

CONVERTER PUMP

STATOR ASSEMBLY

STATOR ROLLER CLUTCH

TURBINE

STATOR SHAFT

INPUT SHAFT

Fig. 12   Cutaway of Super Turbine "300". Some models use a fixed stator

2. Gear noise (1st gear drive range). Check planetary pinions for tooth damage. Check sun gear and front and rear internal gears for tooth finish or damage.
3. Clutch noise during application. Check clutch plates.
4. Sprocket and chain link assembly. Chain link too long (sounds similar to popcorn popping). There will be a rough burr along teeth of drive sprocket if chain link is too long; replace chain link and drive sprocket. Drive or driven sprocket teeth damaged. Engine mounts worn or damaged.

▶ BUICK SUPER TURBINE "300"
1964–69 OLDS JETAWAY
1964–69 PONTIAC 2 SPEED, Fig. 12

Oil Forced Out of Filler Tube

1. Oil level too high; foaming caused by planet carrier running in oil.
2. Water in oil.
3. Leak in pump suction circuits.

Oil Leaks

1. Check extension oil seal.
2. Check outer shift lever oil seal.
3. Check speedometer driven gear fitting.
4. Check oil cooler pipe connections.
5. Check vacuum modulator assembly and case.

No Drive in Any Position

1. Low oil level.
2. Clogged oil strainer screen or suction pipe loose.
3. Defective pressure regulator valve.
4. Front pump defective.
5. Input shaft broken.

Erratic Operation and Slippage Light to Medium Throttle

1. Low oil level.
2. Clogged oil strainer screen.
3. Servo piston seal leaking.
4. Band facing worn.
5. Low band apply struts disengaged or broken.
6. Vacuum modulator.

Engine Speed Flares on Upshifts

1. Low oil level.
2. Improper band adjustment.
3. Clogged oil strainer screen.
4. Forward clutch not fully engaging.
5. Forward clutch plates worn.
6. Forward clutch piston hanging up.
7. Forward clutch drum relief ball not sealing.
8. Vacuum modulator.

Upshifts Harsh

1. Vacuum modulator line broken or disconnected.
2. Vacuum modulator diaphragm leaks.
3. Vacuum modulator valve stuck.

Close Throttle (Coast) Downshift Harsh

1. High engine idle speed.
2. Improper low band adjustment.
3. Downshift timing valve malfunction.
4. High main line pressure. Check the following; a) vacuum modulator line broken or disconnected, b) modulator diaphragm ruptured, c) sticking pressure regulator coast valve, pressure regulator valve or vacuum modulator valve.

Car Creeps Excessively in Drive

1. Idle speed too high.
2. Closed throttle stator switch improperly adjusted (except Tempest and Oldsmobile 6-cylinder models).

Car Creeps in Neutral

1. Forward clutch not released.
2. Low band not released.

No Drive in Reverse

1. Reverse clutch piston stuck.
2. Reverse clutch plates worn out.
3. Reverse clutch seal leaking excessively.
4. Blocked reverse clutch apply orifice.

▶ TURBO HYDRA-MATIC "350" TROUBLES, Fig. 13

No Drive in Drive Range

1. Low oil level (check for leaks).
2. Manual control linkage improperly adjusted.
3. Low oil pressure. Check for blocked strainer, defective pressure regulator, pump assembly or pump drive gear. See that tangs have not been damaged by converter. Check case for porosity in intake bore.
4. Check control valve assembly to be sure manual valve has not been disconnected from inner lever.
5. Forward clutch may be stuck or damaged. Check pump feed circuits to forward clutch, including clutch drum ball check.
6. Roller clutch assembly broken or damaged.

Oil Pressure High or Low

High Pressure:
1. Vacuum line or fittings leaking.
2. Vacuum modulator.
3. Modulator valve.
4. Pressure regulator.
5. Oil pump.

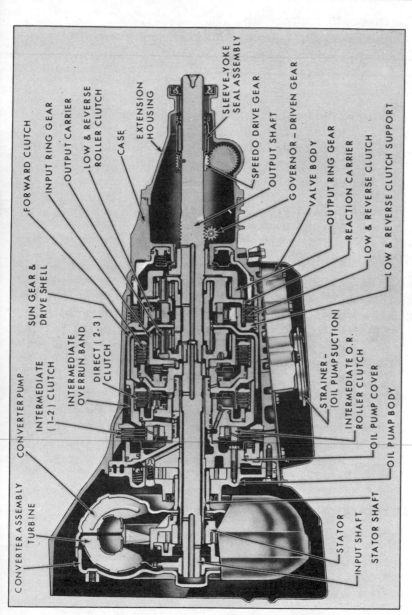

Fig. 13   Cutaway of Turbo Hydra-Matic "350"

Low Pressure:
1. Vacuum line or fittings obstructed.
2. Vacuum modulator.
3. Modulator valve.
4. Pressure regulator.
5. Governor.
6. Oil pump.

1-2 Shift at Full Throttle Only

1. Detent valve may be sticking or linkage may be misadjusted.
2. Vacuum line or fittings leaking.
3. Control valve body gaskets leaking, damaged or incorrectly installed. Detent valve train or 1-2 valve stuck.
4. Check case for porosity.

First Speed Only, No 1-2 Shift

1. Governor valve may be sticking.
2. Driven gear in governor assembly loose, worn or damaged. If driven gear shows damage, check output shaft drive gear for nicks or rough finish.
3. Control valve governor feed channels blocked, or gaskets leaking. 1-2 shift valve train stuck closed.
4. Check case for blocked governor feed channels or for scored governor bore which will allow cross pressure leak. Check case for porosity.
5. Intermediate clutch or seals damaged.
6. Intermediate roller clutch damaged.

1st & 2nd Only, No 2-3 Shift

1. Control valve 2-3 shift train stuck. Valve body gaskets leaking, damaged or incorrectly installed.
2. Pump hub-direct clutch oil seal rings broken or missing.
3. Direct clutch piston seals damaged. Piston ball check stuck or missing.

Moves Forward in Neutral

1. Manual linkage misadjusted.
2. Forward clutch not releasing.

No Drive in Reverse or Slips in Reverse

1. Low oil level.
2. Manual linkage misadjusted.
3. Modulator valve stuck.
4. Modulator and reverse boost valve stuck.
5. Pump hub-direct clutch oil seal rings broken or missing.
6. Direct clutch piston seal cut or missing.
7. Low and reverse clutch piston seal cut or missing.
8. Number 1 check ball missing.
9. Control valve body gaskets leaking or damaged.
10. 2-3 valve train stuck in upshifted position.
11. 1-2 valve train stuck in upshifted position.
12. Intermediate servo piston or pin stuck so intermediate overrun band is applied.
13. Low and reverse clutch piston out or seal damaged.
14. Direct clutch plates burned—may be caused by stuck ball check in piston. Outer seal damaged.
15. Forward clutch not releasing.

Slips in All Ranges

1. Low oil level.
2. Vacuum modulator valve defective or sticking.
3. Filter assembly plugged or leaking.
4. Pressure regulator valve stuck.
5. Pump to case gasket damaged.
6. Check case for cross leaks or porosity.
7. Forward clutch slipping.

Slips 1-2 Shift

1. Low oil level.
2. Vacuum modulator assembly defective.
3. Modulator valve sticking.

4. Pump pressure regulator valve defective.
5. 2-3 accumulator oil ring damaged or missing. 1-2 accumulator oil ring damaged or missing. Case bore damaged.
6. Pump to case gasket mispositioned or damaged.
7. Check case for porosity.
8. Intermediate clutch piston seals damaged. Clutch plates burned.

Rough 1-2 Shift

1. Vacuum modulator—check for loose fittings, restrictions in line or defective modulator assembly.
2. Modulator valve stuck.
3. Valve body regulator or boost valve stuck.
4. Pump to case gasket mispositioned or damaged.
5. Check case for porosity.
6. Check 1-2 accumulator assembly for damaged oil rings, stuck piston, broken or missing spring, or damaged case bore.

Slips 2-3 Shift

1. Low oil level.
2. Modulator valve or vacuum modulator assembly defective.
3. Pump pressure regulator valve or boost valve; pump to case gasket mispositioned.
4. Check case for porosity.
5. Direct clutch piston seals or ball check leaking.

Rough 2-3 Shift

1. High oil pressure. Vacuum leak, modulator valve sticking or pressure regulator or boost valve inoperative.
2. 2-3 accumulator piston stuck, spring broken or missing.

No Engine Braking in Second Speed

1. Intermediate servo or 2-3 accumulator oil rings or bores leaking or accumulator piston stuck.

2. Intermediate overrun band burned or broken.
3. Low oil pressure: Pressure regulator and/or boost valve stuck.

No Engine Braking in 1st Speed

1. Manual low control valve assembly stuck.
2. Low oil pressure: Pressure regulator and/or boost valve stuck.
3. Low and reverse clutch piston inner seal damaged.

No Part Throttle Downshift

1. Oil pressure: Vacuum modulator assembly, modulator valve or pressure regulator valve train malfunctioning.
2. Detent valve and linkage sticking, disconnected or broken.
3. 2-3 shift valve stuck.

No Detent Downshifts

1. 2-3 valve stuck.
2. Detent valve and linkage sticking, disconnected or broken.

Low or High Shift Points

1. Oil pressure: Check engine vacuum at transmission end of the modulator pipe.
2. Vacuum modulator assembly vacuum line connections at engine and transmission modulator valve, pressure regulator valve train.
3. Check governor for sticking valve, restricted or leaking feed holes, damaged pipes of plugged feed line.
4. Detent valve stuck open.
5. 1-2 or 2-3 valve train sticking.
6. Check case for porosity.

Won't Hold in Park

1. Manual linkage misadjusted.
2. Parking brake lever and actuator assembly defective.
3. Parking pawl broken or inoperative.

▶ BUICK TWIN TURBINE TROUBLES, Fig. 14

Engine Stalls While Decelerating Car with Brakes Applied

1. Improper adjustment of throttle dashpot.
2. Engine not properly tuned.

Transmission Oil Foams and Spews Out of Breather

1. Transmission overfilled. If transmission is overfilled, check for blackened condition of oil, indicating leakage of rear axle lubricant into transmission due to defective propeller shaft seals. Check for low oil level in rear axle housing Correct cause of leakage and completely drain and refill transmission.
2. Water in transmission, indicated by overfilled condition and brown color of transmission oil. Water in transmission usually comes from a leaking oil cooler. In this case there may be excessive oil accumulation in top tank of engine radiator. Correct cause of leakage and completely drain and refill transmission.
3. Air leak into hydraulic system at rear oil pump gaskets.

Car Will Not Move in Any Range Rear Wheels Free

1. If car will not move for 1 to 8 minutes after standing overnight, park car for several hours with engine stopped and then check front oil pump pressure. A zero reading until such time as car will move indicates that front pump loses its prime

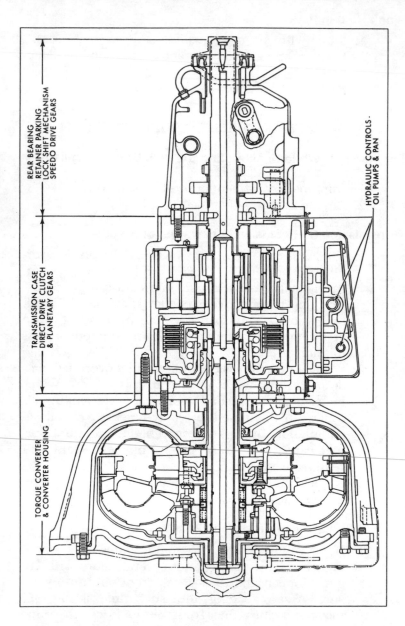

REAR BEARING
RETAINER PARKING
LOCK, SHIFT MECHANISM
SPEEDO DRIVE GEARS

TRANSMISSION CASE
DIRECT DRIVE CLUTCH
& PLANETARY GEARS

TORQUE CONVERTER
& CONVERTER HOUSING

HYDRAULIC CONTROLS -
OIL PUMPS & PAN

Fig. 14 Sectional view of Twin Turbine transmission

due to excessive clearances. Inspect front pump. If condition has existed for some time it is advisable to inspect clutch and bands for excessive wear due to slippage at low apply pressure.

2. If car will not move in any range after extended operation in Reverse it indicates air leakage into pump suction line and suction and excessive clearance at front oil pump. Front oil pump pressure will be very low during period when car will not move. Inspect for air leaks at rear oil pump gaskets. Inspect front oil pump and cover for excessive clearances.

3. Converter one-way clutch slipping.

4. Defective stator shaft.

Car Will Not Move in Any Range—Rear Wheels Locked

1. Parking lock engaged or parking brake applied.

2. Lock up due to broken part in rear axle or transmission.

Car Will Not Move in Direct Drive Only

1. If front oil pump and high accumulator pressures are okay, remove and inspect clutch assembly.

2. If front oil pump pressure is okay but high accumulator pressure is low and accumulator body gasket is not leaking internally, inspect for leaks in reaction flange gasket. If gasket is satisfactory, inspect clutch piston outer seal and ball check, also oil sealing rings on hubs of reaction shaft flange and low drum.

Car Will Not Move in Reverse Only

1. Reverse servo inoperative.

2. Band improperly adjusted or band operating strut has dropped out of place.

3. Reverse ring gear.

Excessive Slip in All Ranges

1. If condition occurs only after operation in Reverse, see Condition 2 under *Car Will Not Move in Any Range—Rear Wheels Free.*
2. Low oil level.
3. Manual control linkage improperly adjusted.
4. If front oil pump pressure is low, remove and inspect pressure regulator valve and all valve and servo body gaskets. If cause is not found remove and inspect front oil pump for wear or excessive clearances. Inspect pump cover and reaction shaft flange gaskets for leaks.
5. Defective sun gear and sprag assembly.

Excessive Slip in Direct Drive Only

1. Manual control linkage improperly adjusted.
2. Leak at high accumulator gasket, indicated by low oil pressure at high accumulator.
3. If above items are okay, remove and inspect clutch plates, sealing rings and clutch piston. Inspect for stuck check ball in piston.

Excessive Slip in Low Only

1. Manual control linkage improperly adjusted.
2. Low-band improperly adjusted.
3. If pressure at low accumulator is low, check for leak at accumulator body gasket. If gasket is okay remove valve and servo body and check for gasket leaks and condition of low servo piston seal.
4. Low band and drum scored or worn.

Excessive Slip in Reverse Only

1. Manual control linkage improperly adjusted.
2. Reverse band improperly adjusted. Check for strut out of place or broken anchor.
3. If front oil pump pressure is low remove valve

and servo body and check for gasket leaks and condition of reverse servo piston seal.

4. Reverse band and ring gear scored or worn.

Car Creeps in Neutral

1. Manual control linkage improperly adjusted.
2. Remove valve and servo body and check for low servo piston sticking up.
3. Remove clutch and inspect for sticking, warped or improperly assembled clutch plates. Note whether "dish" of steel plates is in same direction on all plates. If creep occurs only when engine is accelerated to about 2500 rpm, pay particular attention to condition of check balls at vents in clutch piston and reaction shaft flange.

Car Creeps Forward in Reverse or Backward in Low

Manual control linkage improperly adjusted.

Low-to-Direct Shift Abnormally Rough, or Slip Occurs

1. If high accumulator presure is low, remove accumulator and check body gaskets. Check for accumulator piston sticking down. Top land of piston must be fully visible through top port in body.
2. If accumulator and gasket are okay, inspect for leaks in valve and servo body gaskets.
3. Low band improperly adjusted.
4. Binding or worn clutch plates.

Excessive Chatter or Clunk When
Starting in Low or Reverse

NOTE: A very slight chatter just as car starts to move in reverse, which disappears as soon as car is in motion, may be considered normal. A slight clunk when shifting into Low or Reverse is also normal.

1. Check engine and transmission mountings for tightness. Inspect for broken rubber thrust pad at transmission mounting.

2. Low or Reverse band improperly adjusted.
3. If conditions 1 and 2 do not correct the trouble, direct drive clutch may be dragging. Remove clutch and inspect for sticking, warped, or improperly assembled clutch plates. Note whether "dish" of steel plates is in same direction on all plates.
4. Inspect for excessive wear of reverse ring gear bushing. Check for foreign matter in planet pinion needle bearings.

Hard Shifting Out of Parking

This condition is caused by binding of transmission shift rod in shift idler lever. If a burr exists on shift rod where it enters idler lever, remove burr with a file. If idler lever is distorted, replace the lever.

TRANSMISSION NOISES

When diagnosing abnormal noises in the transmission, consideration should be given to the parts that are in motion when the noise occurs. The presence or absence of noise in each range should be noted so that the parts which cause the noise can be determined by a process of elimination.

Hum or Low Whine in Neutral or Parking

A hum or low whine in Neutral or Park is normal since all planetary gears are free to rotate without the steadying effect of a load. Some hum also may be expected in Low and Reverse.

Low Growl in Transmission

A low growl in transmission which disappears in several minutes after engine is started, following extended parking in extremely cold weather is caused by cavitation of the cold oil. This is a normal condition which requires no correction.

Buzzing Noise

A buzzing noise can be caused by low oil level, or by the

front pump delivery check valve seating on the edge of the gasket between valves and servo bodies.

A buzzing noise, noticeable in Park and Neutral, may be caused by excessive clearance of pressure regulator valve in valve body or an oversize orifice in valve land. Correction requires replacement of valve.

Clicking Noise in All Ranges

This may be caused by a foreign object going through the converter. A clicking noise only when car is in motion may be caused by the parking lock pawl contacting the ratchet wheel due to improper manual control linkage adjustment.

Abnormal Hum or Whine in All Ranges

This condition may be attributed to worn parts or excessive clearances in the front oil pump. Noise caused by the front pump will increase in Low and will diminish at car speeds above 45 mph in Direct Drive. It increases and decreases with engine speed in all ranges. When excessive clearances exist in front oil pump, a pressure test will usually indicate low front pump pressure.

Abnormal Hum or Whine in All Ranges but Direct Drive

This may be attributed to conditions in the planetary gear train since these gears are locked in Direct Drive but either idling or transmitting power in all other ranges.

Squealing or Screeching

Squealing or screeching immediately following installation of front oil pump parts indicates that the driving gear has been installed backwards. This condition should be corrected without further operation of the transmission as severe damage will result.

Whistling Noise

A whistling noise which occurs during low speed acceleration in Drive, Low and Reverse, accompanied by unsatisfactory transmission performance indicates cavitation of oil due to incomplete filling of torque convector. Remove valve and servo body assembly and check for restrictions in passages leading to torque converter. If these passages are clear, check passages in reaction shaft flange.

A whistling noise during low speed acceleration in Drive, Low and Reverse but with otherwise satisfactory transmission performance may be caused by thin, weak, or cracked turbine vanes, or vanes which are bent over at the exit edges. Such vanes will vibrate under load, causing a whistle. Replacement of the turbine is required for correction.

▶ CHEVROLET POWERGLIDE & TORQUE DRIVE TROUBLES TYPE WITH ALUMINUM CASE

Oil Forced Out Filler Tube

1. Oil level too high; aeration and foaming caused by planet carrier running in oil.
2. Water in oil.
3. Leak in pump suction circuits.

Oil Leaks

1. Transmission case and extension: extension oil seal, shifter shaft oil seal, speedometer driven gear fitting, pressure taps, oil cooler pipe connections, vacuum modulator and case, transmission oil pan gasket.
2. A very smoky exhaust indicates a ruptured vacuum modulator diaphragm.
3. Converter cover pan; front pump attaching bolts, pump seal ring, pump oil seal, plugged oil drain in front pump, porosity in transmission case.

No Drive in Any Position

1. Low oil level.
2. Clogged oil suction screen.

3. Defective pressure regulator valve.
4. Front pump defective.
5. Input shaft broken.
6. Front pump priming valve stuck.

Erratic Operation and Slippage—Light to Medium Throttle

1. Low oil level.
2. Clogged oil suction screen.
3. Improper band adjustment.
4. Band facing worn.
5. Low band apply linkage disengaged or broken.
6. Servo apply passage blocked.
7. Servo piston ring broken or leaking.
8. Converter stator not holding (rare).

Engine Speed Flares on Upshift

1. Low oil level.
2. Improper band adjustment.
3. Clogged oil suction screen.
4. High clutch partially applied—blocked feed orifice.
5. High clutch plates worn.
6. High clutch seals leak.
7. High clutch piston hung up.
8. High clutch drum relief ball not sealing.
9. Vacuum modulator line plugged.
10. Vacuum modulator defective.

Will Not Upshift

1. Maladjusted manual valve lever.
2. Throttle valve stuck or maladjusted.
3. No rear oil pump output caused by stuck priming valve, sheared drive pin or defective pump.
4. Defective governor.
5. Stuck low-drive valve.

Harsh Upshifts

1. Throttle valve linkage improperly adjusted.

2. Vacuum modulator line broken or disconnected.
3. Vacuum modulator diaphragm leaks.
4. Vacuum modulator valve stuck.
5. Hydraulic modulator valve stuck.
6. Improper low band adjustment.

Harsh Closed Throttle (Coast) Downshifts

1. High engine idle speed.
2. Improper band adjustment.
3. Vacuum modulator line broken or disconnected.
4. Modulator diaphragm ruptured.
5. Sticking hydraulic modulator valve, pressure regulator valve or vacuum modulator valve.
6. Downshift timing valve malfunction.

No Downshift (Direct-to-Low) Accelerator Floored

1. Throttle control linkage improperly adjusted.
2. Sticking shifter valve or throttle and detent valve.

Car Creeps in Neutral

1. Manual control linkage improperly adjusted.
2. High clutch or low band not released.

No Drive in Reverse

1. Manual control linkage improperly adjusted.
2. Reverse clutch piston stuck.
3. Reverse clutch plates worn out.
4. Reverse clutch leaking excessively.
5. Blocked reverse clutch apply orifice.

Improper Shift Points

1. Throttle valve linkage improperly adjusted.
2. Incorrectly adjusted throttle valve.
3. Defective governor.
4. Rear pump priming valve stuck, 1962–66.

Unable to Push Start, 1962–66

1. Rear pump drive gear not engaged with drive pin on output shaft.

2. Drive pin sheared off or missing.
3. Rear pump priming valve not sealing.
4. Rear pump defective.

▶ CHEVROLET POWERGLIDE TYPE WITH CAST IRON CASE

Oil Forced Out Filler Tube

1. Oil level too high.
2. Damaged suction pipe seal.
3. Ears on suction pipe retainer bent.
4. Bore for suction pipe in housing too deep.
5. Sand hole in suction bore in transmission case or housing.
6. Sand hole in suction cavity of valve body.
7. Water in oil.

Oil Leaks

1. At transmission case side cover.
2. At low-drive valve body and transmission case.
3. At servo cover and transmission case.
4. At transmission housing and case.
5. At front of flywheel housing.
6. At oil cooler pipes and connections.
7. At transmission case oil seals.
8. Ruptured diaphragm in vacuum modulator.
9. At O-ring seal between converter cover and pump.
10. At front O-ring seal and front pump oil seal.
11. Plugged oil drain in front pump.
12. Leaks between front pump and converter cavity due to sand hole in housing.

Car Won't Move in Any Range—Rear Wheels Free

1. If car will not move in any range after extended operation in reverse it indicates air leakage into suction lines and excessive clearances at front oil pump. Front pump pressure will be very low during

period when car will not move. Inspect for air leaks at rear pump gasket.

2. If car will not move for several minutes after standing overnight, park car for several hours with engine stopped and then check front pump pressure. A zero pressure will indicate that the front pump loses its prime due to excessive clearances. If condition has existed for some time it is advisable to inspect clutch and bands for excessive wear due to slippage.
3. Broken internal parts.
4. Converter one-way clutch slipping.
5. Defective stator shaft.

Won't Move in Any Range—Rear Wheels Locked

1. Parking lock pawl engaged.
2. Parking brake applied.
3. Lock up due to broken part in transmission or rear axle.

Won't Move in Reverse

1. Low band needs adjusting.
2. Clutch relief valve stuck.
3. Clutch plates binding in hub or flange.
4. Clutch plates not properly installed.
5. Clutch piston stuck.
6. Reverse band strut broken.
7. Broken reverse band. This problem, which occurs on 1958 V8's, is generally caused by harsh application of reverse pressure. To prevent its reoccurrence a pressure regulator and damper valve kit (Part No. 3759998) is available for installation. An alternate remedy is to remove the reverse servo and pipe tap a ⅛" plug in the reverse oil passage. Then drill a 1/16" hole in the plug to restrict the oil pressure and soften the application of the reverse band.

Slips When Transmission is Hot

1. No clutch pressure; clutch drum bushing needs replacing.

Excessive Slip in All Ranges

1. Low oil level.
2. Throttle linkage needs adjusting.
3. Oil suction pipe not seating properly.
4. Oil suction screen clogged.
5. Front pump worn or damaged.
6. Faulty pressure regulator valve or gasket.

Excessive Slip in Manual Low and
1st Gear of Drive Range

1. Improper linkage adjustment.
2. Improper low band adjustment.
3. Broken low band.
4. Accumulator band stuck.
5. Broken low servo piston ring.
6. Worn clutch drum.
7. Defective servo-to-case gasket.
8. Defective valve body gaskets.

Excessive Slip in Reverse Only

1. Improper linkage adjustment.
2. Improper reverse band adjustment or broken band.
3. No oil pressure due to stuck accumulator valve.
4. Broken reverse servo piston ring.
5. Defective valve body gaskets.

Car Creeps in Neutral

1. Improper manual linkage adjustment.
2. Low band adjusted too tight.
3. Clutch inoperative due to:
   Plates not properly assembled.
   Plates sticking.
   Clutch relief valve stuck closed.

Defective valve body gasket.

Control lever not attached to manual control valve inside transmission.

Car Creeps Forward in Reverse or Backward in Low

1. Manual linkage improperly adjusted.

Low-to-Direct Shift Very Rough

1. Improper low band adjustment.
2. Modulator vacuum line leaking.
3. Worn clutch plates.
4. Clutch plates binding in drum or flange.
5. Inoperative accumulator dump valve.

Engine Races on Low-to-Direct Shift

1. Modulator spring weak.
2. Clutch plates worn or burned.
3. Oil passage to clutch restricted.

Rough Shift Direct-to-Low

1. Vacuum modulator valve stuck.
2. Improper low band adjustment.
3. High speed downshift timing valve inoperative.

No Upshift in Drive Range

1. Broken rear pump drive pin.
2. Defective governor.
3. Stuck shift valve.
4. Clutch plates worn or burned.

No Shift Direct-to-Low With Accelerator Floored

1. Throttle linkage improperly adjusted.
2. Sticking shifter valve or shuttle and detent valve.

Rough Shift Neutral-to-Reverse

1. Engine idling speed too high.
2. Improper reverse band adjustment.
3. Accumulator piston stuck closed.
4. Excessive end play in transmission main shaft.

Chatter in Manual Low and 1st Gear Drive Range

1. Improper low band adjustment.
2. Worn low band or drum.
3. Defective clutch plates.
4. Clutch piston stuck.
5. Clutch relief valve stuck.

Chatter in Reverse

1. Improper reverse band adjustment.
2. Worn reverse band or drum.
3. Worn or damaged reverse ring gear bushing.
4. Worn or damaged transmission case rear bushing.

Buzzing in All Ranges

1. Low oil level.
2. Front or rear pumps not functioning properly.

Ringing Noise in Converter

1. Low oil level.
2. Oil suction pipe damaged or not seating properly.
3. Defective pressure regulator valve.
4. Front oil pump worn.

▶ CHEVROLET TURBOGLIDE TROUBLES

No Drive in Any Range

1. Low oil level.
2. Front pump defective or assembled backwards.
3. Front pump priming ball not seating.
4. Defective converter pump.
5. Converter one-way clutch slipping.
6. Defective stator shaft.

No Drive Except In Grade Retard

1. Both overrun clutches assembled backwards.

No Drive Except in Grade Retard and Reverse. Cannot Load Engine in Drive

1. Outer overrun clutch assembled backwards.
2. Forward and neutral clutch not applied due to severe leakage in forward clutch hydraulic circuit.

Drive is Poor at Low Speed, No Reverse, Grade Retard Normal

1. Inner overrun clutch assembled backwards.
2. Stator overrun clutch not holding.

Car Drives Very Slightly in Neutral, Reverse Normal

1. Neutral clutch not released.

Car Drives Normal in Neutral and Drive at Low Speeds, No Reverse

1. Forward clutch not released.

Transmission Will Not Shift to Performance Stator Angle

1. Stator control linkage out of adjustment.
2. Converter charging pressure is low for one of the following reasons:
   (a) Leakage which will reduce line pressure enough to cause pressure regulator valve to shut off converter "in" line.
   (b) Leakage in converter circuit.
   (c) Discharge orifice in transfer plate plugged.
   (d) Damaged or leaking seal rings on second turbine shaft. Damage to front ring allows converter "out" pressure to leak to stator passage. Damage to middle ring allows neutral pressure to leak to converter "out" passage.

Unable to Push Start

1. Rear oil pump drive pin broken.

Clutch Slippage on Wide Open Throttle Starts

1. Low oil pressure due to leakage. Especially check forward pressure tube O-ring.
2. Mechanical interference which will prevent forward piston from fully applying.
3. Forward clutch facing failure.

Grade Retard Slow to Apply

1. Control linkage out of adjustment preventing manual valve getting into grade retard position.
2. Low pressure resulting from leakage. Check pressure tube O-ring seals and other O-ring seals.
3. Mechanical interference of grade retard piston.
4. Glazed grade retard plates.

No Drive, Reverse Normal, No Grade Retard

1. Reverse clutch not disengaged.

Grade Retard Brakes Violently

1. Vacuum hose disconnected.
2. Vacuum modulator diaphragm ruptured or hose disconnected.

Shifts From Standstill Very Slowly

1. Check linkage to ascertain that shift lever is positioned by transmission detents.
2. Accumulator control valve stuck closed.
3. Leakage in hydraulic system. Check pressure tube O-ring seals and other seals and gaskets.
4. Front pump priming ball seating poorly (1959–60).
5. Front pump side clearance excessive.

Shifts From Standstill Very Harsh and Fast

1. Accumulator control valve spring too strong or valve stuck open.
2. Vacuum modulator diaphragm ruptured.

3. Vacuum hose disconnected.
4. Excessively high idle speed.
5. Defective neutral accumulator spring (1959–60).
6. Kinked vacuum to modulator supply hose.

Excess Vibration in Neutral

1. Converter and flywheel not in proper alignment.

Transmission Operates OK When Cold but Not When Hot

1. If transmission operates properly when cold but has excessive slip when hot, along with no reverse, it indicates that the sun gear free wheeling sprags are worn.

▶ CORVAIR & 1961–63 PONTIAC TEMPEST

Oil Forced Out Filler Tube

1. Oil level too high causing planet carrier to run in oil and cause foam.
2. Oil pickup pipe split or not sealed, allowing air in system.

No Drive in Any Position

1. Low oil level.
2. Clogged oil suction pipe screen.
3. Broken or disconnected manual valve cable.
4. Defective pressure regulator valve.
5. Front pump defective.
6. Rear pump check valve, check valve poppet, or rear pump priming ball not seating. Both must occur for possible malfunction.
7. Defective line pressure limit valve.
8. Front pump shaft disengaged at either converter or pump gear.
9. Front pump priming ball not seating.

Erratic Operation or Slippage (Light to Medium Throttle)

1. Low oil level.
2. Clogged pickup pipe screen.
3. Improper band adjustment.
4. Band facing worn.
5. Low band apply linkage disengaged or broken.
6. Servo piston apply passage blocked.
7. Servo piston ring broken or missing.
8. Converter stator not holding (rare).

Engine Speed Flares on Upshift

1. Low oil level.
2. Improper band adjustment.
3. Clogged oil suction screen.
4. High clutch partially applied (blocked feed orifice).
5. High clutch plates worn.
6. High clutch seals leak.
7. High clutch piston hung up.
8. High clutch relief ball not seating.
9. Vacuum modulator hose plugged.
10. Vacuum modulator defective.

Will Not Upshift

1. Maladjusted manual valve lever.
2. Throttle valve stuck or maladjusted.
3. No rear pump output caused by stuck priming valve, sheared pin or defective pump.
4. Defective governor.
5. Stuck low-drive valve.

Harsh Upshifts

1. Throttle valve linkage improperly adjusted.
2. Vacuum modulator hose broken or disconnected.
3. Vacuum modulator diaphragm leaks.
4. Vacuum modulator valve stuck.

5. Hydraulic modulator valve stuck.
6. Improper low band adjustment.

Harsh Closed Throttle Downshifts

1. High engine idle speed.
2. Improper low band adjustment.
3. Vacuum modulator hose disconnected or broken.
4. Vacuum modulator diaphragm ruptured.
5. Vacuum modulator valve stuck.
6. Sticking valves in valve body (pressure regulator or hydraulic modulator valves).

Creeps in Neutral

1. Manual linkage improperly adjusted.
2. High clutch or low band not released.

No Drive in Reverse

1. Manual valve linkage improperly adjusted (cable).
2. Reverse clutch piston stuck.
3. Reverse clutch plates worn out.
4. Reverse clutch leaking excessively.
5. Blocked reverse clutch apply orifice.

Improper Shift Points

1. Throttle valve linkage improperly adjusted.
2. Incorrectly adjusted TV valve.
3. Governor defective.
4. Rear pump priming valve stuck.

Unable to Push Start

1. Rear pump drive gear not engaged with drive pins on planet carrier hub.
2. Drive pin sheared off or missing.
3. Rear pump priming ball not seating.
4. Rear pump defective.

▶ DUAL COUPLING HYDRAMATIC, Fig. 15

Slips in 1st & 3rd

1. Front sprag clutch slipping.
2. Front sprag clutch broken.

Slips in or Misses 2nd & 4th

1. Front unit torus cover seals leaking.
2. Front unit torus cover exhaust valves sticking or missing.
3. Front unit torus cover feed restriction or leak.
4. Front unit torus cover signal restriction or leak.
5. Low oil pressure.
6. Coupling valve sticking.
7. Sticking valves or dirt in valve body.
8. Coupling snap ring improperly installed or missing.
9. Limit valve.
10. Coupling passage restricted or leaking.
11. Front unit torus vanes damaged.

Slips in All D Ranges

1. Manual linkage.
2. Neutral clutch slipping or burned.
3. Neutral clutch apply restricted or leaking (case support or valve body).
4. Incorrect number of neutral clutch plates.
5. Low oil pressure.
6. Control valve.
7. Torus members (check valve).
8. Intake pipe O-ring damaged or missing.
9. Pressure regulator valve stuck in pump.
10. Pump slide stuck.

Slips in 1st & 2nd (D Range)

1. Rear sprag clutch slipping or improperly assembled.

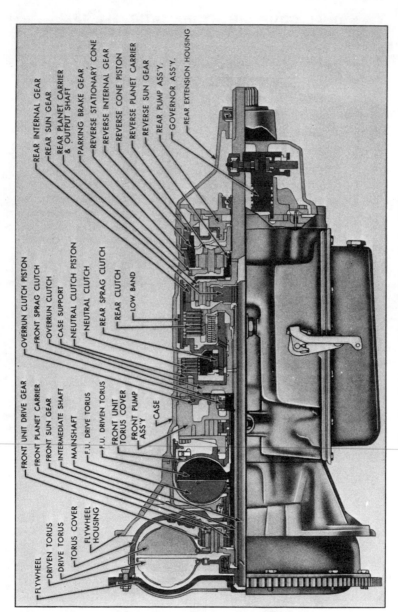

Fig. 15 Cutaway of Dual Coupling Hydra-Matic

2. Rear sprag clutch broken.
3. Neutral clutch burned, restricted, piston sticking.

Slips in 3rd & 4th

1. Rear unit clutch slipping or burned.
2. Rear unit clutch apply restricted or O-ring leaking.
3. Incorrect number of clutch plates (rear).
4. Accumulator.
5. Center support, leak at 2-3 passage.
6. Low oil pressure.
7. Accumulator valve stuck (3rd only).

Slips in 3rd in Drive Right on Coast

1. Overrun clutch slipping or burned.
2. Overrun clutch apply restricted or leaking.
3. Sticking valves or dirt in valve body.
4. Overrun clutch passages restricted or leaking.

Slips In 1st & 2nd in Low Range on Coast

1. Low servo apply restricted or leaking.
2. Low band not anchored to case or broken.
3. Low servo piston and rod binding in case or servo and accumulator body.
4. Band facing worn or loose.
5. Anchor dowel pin missing or loose in case.

No Drive in D Range

1. Manual linkage incorrectly adjusted.
2. Manual valve not engaged with drive pin.
3. Low oil pressure.
4. Pressure regulator stuck.
5. Pump intake pipe improperly installed.
6. Front sprag broken, pump bushing, front unit drive torus shaft.
7. Front and/or rear sprag incorrectly installed.
8. Rear sprag broken.
9. Front sprag inner race broken.
10. Rear sprag outer race broken.

11. Neutral clutch plates burned.
12. Neutral clutch piston.
13. Control valve.
14. Pump.

Erratic or No Upshifts

1. Governor valves stuck.
2. Broken governor rings.
3. Sticking valves or dirt in valve body.
4. G-2 bushing turned.

Misses in 2nd

1. Governor boost valve stuck closed.
2. Transition valve stuck away from plate.
3. Sticking valves or dirt in valve body.
4. Governor sticking.

Misses in 3rd

1. Transition valve sticking.
2. Sticking valves or dirt in valve body.
3. TV adjustment—too long.
4. Rear clutch.
5. Transition valve spring.

Locks Up in 2nd & 4th

1. Front sprag clutch broken or reversed.
2. Overrun clutch applied or sticking.

Locks Up in 3rd & 4th

1. Rear sprag clutch broken.
2. Low band not releasing.

Rough 2-3 Shift

1. Accumulator valve stuck.
2. Accumulator piston stuck.
3. Accumulator gasket broken or missing.
4. Restricted or leaking oil passages.

   5. Broken accumulator spring.
   6. Broken or leaking piston oil seal rings.
   7. Control valve.
   8. TV adjusted incorrectly.
   9. Rear clutch pack.
  10. Case passages; TV oil, 2-3 oil, leaks or restrictions.

Upshifts High

1. Throttle linkage adjusted short.
2. Governor valves sticking.
3. Broken governor rings.
4. Sticking valves or dirt in valve body.
5. Leaking or restricted main line feed to governor.

Upshifts Low

1. Throttle linkage adjusted long.
2. Governor valves sticking.
3. Broken governor rings.
4. Sticking valves or dirt in valve body.
5. Leaking TV oil.

No Reverse, Slips or Locks Up

1. Manual linkage incorrectly adjusted.
2. Manual valve not engaged with drive pin.
3. Reverse piston apply restricted or leaking.
4. Low oil pressure.
5. Pressure regulator.
6. Neutral clutch not released.
7. Flash restricting neutral clutch exhaust port on manual body.

Selector Lever Won't Go in Reverse

1. Governor valves sticking.
2. Broken governor rings.
3. Reverse blocker piston stuck.
4. Manual linkage interference.

Reverse Drive in Neutral

1. Reverse stationary cone sticking.

Delayed 1-2 Shift

1. Coupling valve sticking.
2. Governor boost valve sticking.
3. G-1 valve sticking.
4. Wrong spring on coupling valve.

Drive in Low Range Only

1. Rear sprag broken.
2. Neutral clutch not applying.

No Forced Downshifts 4-3 or 3-2

1. Control valve.
2. Linkage.

2-3 Runaway

1. 2-3 passage in center bearing support.
2. Plug out of accumulator.
3. Rear clutch burned.
4. Valve body; transition valve, case passages (2-3 circuit).

Won't Go Into Park

1. Parking links broken.
2. Mechanical interference.
3. Manual linkage.
4. Parking pawl.

Starts in 2nd Speed

1. Valves sticking.
2. Governor sticking.
3. Governor boost valve stuck.

Drives Forward in Reverse & Neutral

1. Neutral clutch piston stuck in applied position.

Lunges Forward Before Back Up When Placing Selector in Reverse

1. G-2 plunger stuck in outward position.
2. Restricted neutral clutch release oil.

NOISE DIAGNOSIS

P, R, N, D 1st and 3rd

1. Front unit planetary gears.

P, R, N, D 1st and 2nd

1. Rear unit planetary gears.

All Ranges, Especially During Warm Up

1. Pump noisy; cut O-ring on intake pipe, cut O-ring on cooler sleeves.

1-2 and 3-4 with Hot Oil

1. Front unit coupling leaks.

All Ranges—Loaded Only in Reverse

1. Reverse planetary gears.

Clicking—Low Speed Forward

1. Pressure regulator.
2. Low oil pressure or level.
3. Coupling valve.
4. Governor.

Buzzing

1. Pressure regulator.
2. Oil pressure.
3. Throttle valve.
4. Rear bearing (at about 35 mph).

Rattle or Buzz Under Light Load in 3rd and 4th

1. Torus cover; damper spring.

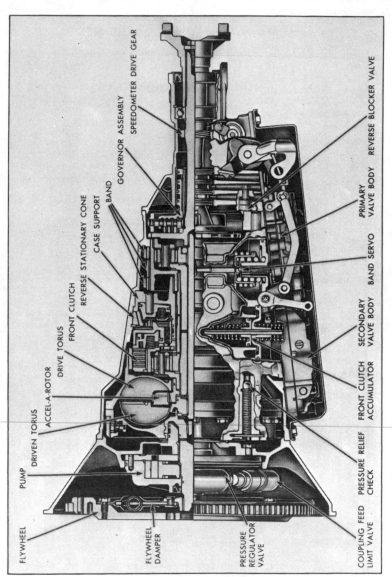

Fig. 16   Cross section of 1963 transmission

FLYWHEEL

PUMP

DRIVEN TORUS

ACCEL-A-ROTOR

DRIVE TORUS

FRONT CLUTCH

REVERSE STATIONARY CONE

CASE SUPPORT

BAND

GOVERNOR ASSEMBLY

SPEEDOMETER DRIVE GEAR

REVERSE BLOCKER VALVE

PRIMARY VALVE BODY

BAND SERVO

SECONDARY VALVE BODY

FRONT CLUTCH ACCUMULATOR

PRESSURE RELIEF CHECK

COUPLING FEED LIMIT VALVE

PRESSURE REGULATOR VALVE

FLYWHEEL DAMPER

Squeak When Engaging Reverse

1. Low oil pressure or leak in front clutch overrun piston.
2. Rear pump (prior to 1959).

Vibration

1. Flywheel balance.
2. Torus cover balance.
3. Front unit assembly balance.
4. Rear brake drum balance.

▶ OLDS F-85 HYDRA-MATIC, Fig. 16

Low Oil Pressure

1. Boost plug stuck.
2. Pressure regulator valve stuck or spring damaged.
3. Strainer O-ring damaged.
4. Manual valve misaligned with pin.
5. Internal leaks.
6. Control valve assembly may have sticking valves.
7. Leak in pump suction circuit.
8. Front pump defective.
9. Ball check valve in control valve assembly defective.

High Oil Pressure

1. Pressure regulator valve may be stuck or damaged.
2. Boost plug sticking.
3. Manual valve misaligned with pin.
4. Sticking valve in control valve assembly.
5. Pump slide sticking; cover-to-slide clearance too great.

No Drive in Drive Range

1. Low oil level.
2. Low oil pressure.

3. Manual control linkage improperly adjusted.
4. Adjust or replace servo band.
5. Sticking valve in valve body.
6. Leaking or restricted circuit in servo, coupling, case cover, governor.
7. Reverse clutch.

Missing All Shifts

1. Sticking governor valve.
2. Sticking valve in control valve assembly.
3. Clutch not applying.

Drive in 2nd and 3rd Only

1. Sticking valve in control valve assembly.
2. Clutch locked—too many plates.

Drive in 1st and 3rd Only, 1961

1. Sticking valve in control valve assembly.
2. Coupling not emptying.

Drive in 1st Only, 1962–63

1. Sticking valve in control valve assembly.
2. Inspect front clutch and accumulator for leaks.
3. Governor rings broken, worn ring lands, sticking valves.

Drive in 1st and 2nd Only

1. G-2 governor valve sticking.
2. Sticking valve in control valve assembly.

Drive in 3rd Only

1. Sticking valve in control valve assembly.
2. Band not applying (1961).
3. Governor valves sticking.

Drive in Neutral (Reverse or Forward)

1. Internal linkage (manual) engaging.
2. Mispositioned front clutch.
3. Reverse cone clutch not applying.

No Reverse

1. Manual linkage (internal) mispositioned.
2. Low oil pressure.
3. Reverse cone clutch not engaging.
4. Restricted passage.
5. Band not releasing.

Rough 1-2 Shift

1. TV linkage maladjusted.
2. Stuck valves in control valve assembly.
3. Defective accumulator (sticking parts).
4. Coupling not emptying fast enough.
5. Front clutch slipping.
6. 1-2 oil passages restricted.

Rough 2-3 Shift

1. Band not releasing quickly.
2. Sticking servo parts.

Slipping in All Ranges

1. Low oil pressure.

Slipping 1-2 Shift

1. TV linkage adjusted too long.
2. Low oil pressure.
3. Check for restrictions or sticking accumulator parts.
4. Stuck valves in control valve assembly.
5. Slipping band.
6. Front clutch (check number of plates).
7. Restricted 1-2 oil passages.

Slipping 2-3 Shift

1. Stuck valves in control valve assembly.
2. Coupling not filling fast enough (1961).
3. Front clutch slipping.

Slipping 3-4 Shift, 1962–63

1. Stuck valves in control valve assembly.
2. Front clutch slipping.

No Engine Braking

1. Stuck valves in control valve assembly.
2. Slipping band.
3. Servo not applying.

No Part Throttle or Detent Downshifts

1. TV linkage adjusted too long.
2. Stuck valves in control valve assembly.
3. Accelerator travel short.
4. Governor valves sticking.

Selector Valve Won't Go into Reverse

1. Manual linkage (internal) mispositioned.
2. Reverse blocker valve stuck open.
3. Governor G-2 valve sticking.

Selector Lever Won't Go into Park

1. Parking linkage broken, improperly assembled, distorted.
2. Manual linkage maladjusted.

Drives Forward in Reverse

1. Manual linkage (internal) improperly assembled or distorted.

High Upshifts

1. TV linkage adjusted short.
2. Stuck valve in control valve assembly.
3. Sticking governor valve.
4. TV lever bent.
5. TV pressure high.

6. Line pressure high.
7. Governor oil passage restricted.

Upshifts Low

1. TV linkage adjusted long.
2. Stuck valve in control valve assembly.
3. Governor valve sticking.
4. TV lever bent.
5. TV pressure low.
6. Line pressure low.
7. Governor oil passage restricted.

Hanging in 2nd—Engine Stall upon Stop

1. Sticking governor valve.
2. Sticking valve in control valve assembly.
3. TV linkage adjusted short.
4. Clutch not releasing.

▶ ROTO HYDRA-MATIC 375 Fig. 17

High Oil Pressure

1. Pressure regulator valve stuck or damaged.
2. Boost plug sticking.
3. Manual valve misaligned with pin.
4. Sticking valve in control valve body.
5. Pump slide sticking; cover-to-slide clearance too great.

Low Oil Pressure

1. Oil level low.
2. Boost plug stuck.
3. Pressure regulator valve stuck or spring damaged.
4. Strainer O-ring seal damaged.
5. Manual valve misaligned with pin.
6. Internal leaks.
7. Sticking valves in control valve body.

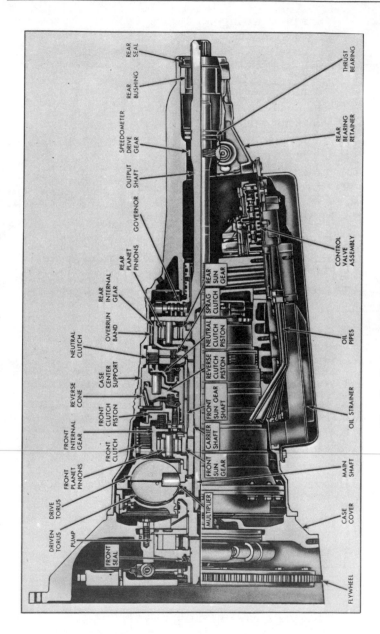

Fig. 17 Cross section of transmission

8. Leak in pump suction circuit.
9. Front pump defective.
10. Ball check valve in control valve assembly defective.

No Drive in Drive Range

1. Low oil level.
2. Low oil pressure.
3. Manual control linkage.
4. Control valve assembly.
5. Leaking or restricted circuit in coupling, neutral clutch, case cover, governor.
6. Reverse clutch.
7. Sprag or race.

First Speed Only

1. Governor.
2. Control valve assembly.
3. Front clutch.

Drive in Third Only

1. Governor.
2. Control valve assembly,

Drive 3rd and 4th Only

1. Control valve assembly.
2. Governor.

No Fourth

1. Governor.
2. Control valve assembly.
3. Oil passages in clutch, accumulator, compensator, drive passages or TV passages.

Drive in Neutral—Forward or Reverse

1. Manual linkage improperly adjusted.
2. Neutral clutch.
3. Reverse clutch.

No Reverse

1. Manual linkage improperly adjusted.
2. Low oil pressure.
3. Reserve clutch.
4. Governor.

Slipping All Ranges

1. Low oil level.
2. Low oil pressure.
3. Coupling.

Slipping 2-3 Shift

1. Throttle linkage improperly adjusted.
2. Low oil level.
3. Low oil pressure.
4. Leaking or restricted circuit in front clutch, accumulator, compensator, TV passage, drive passage.
5. Control valve assembly.

Rough 1-2 Shift

1. Neutral clutch by-pass valve broken.

Rough 2-3 Shift

1. Throttle linkage improperly adjusted.
2. Control valve assembly.
3. Leaking or restricted circuit in front clutch, accumulator, compensator, TV passage, drive passage.

Slipping 3-4 Shift

1. Control valve assembly.
2. Leaking or restricted circuit in coupling, front clutch, accumulator, compensator, TV passage, drive passage.

No Engine Braking—3rd or Low

1. Control valve assembly.
2. Overrun band servo.

No Part Throttle or Detent Downshifts

1. Throttle linkage improperly adjusted; accelerator pedal height.
2. Control valve assembly.
3. Governor.

Selector Lever Won't Go into Reverse

1. Manual linkage improperly adjusted.
2. Reverse blocker piston.
3. Governor.

Selector Lever Won't Go into Park

1. Manual linkage improperly adjusted.
2. Parking linkage (internal).

Forward Drive in Reverse

1. Manual linkage improperly adjusted.
2. Manual valve.
3. Neutral clutch.

Low or High Upshifts

1. Throttle linkage improperly adjusted.
2. TV pressure high.
3. Governor.

▶ CHRYSLER POWERFLITE TROUBLES, Fig. 18
POOR SHIFT QUALITY

Harsh Shift from Neutral to Reverse

1. Reverse band adjustment.
2. Reverse piston, sleeve, etc.
3. Reverse band, lever, strut, etc.
4. Incorrect engine idle speed.

Harsh Shift from Neutral to Drive

1. Throttle linkage adjustment.
2. Kickdown piston, guide, etc.
3. Incorrect engine idle speed.

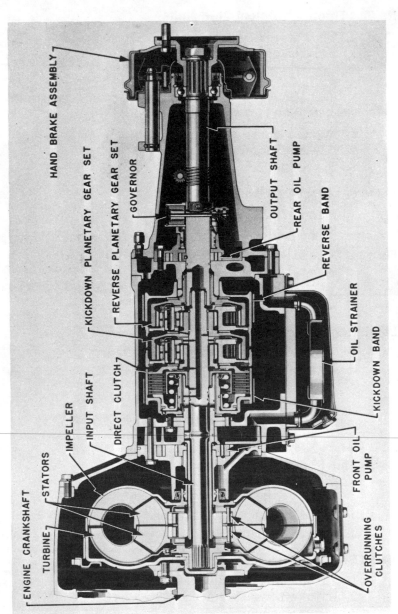

ENGINE CRANKSHAFT

TURBINE

STATORS

IMPELLER

INPUT SHAFT

DIRECT CLUTCH

HAND BRAKE ASSEMBLY

KICKDOWN PLANETARY GEAR SET

REVERSE PLANETARY GEAR SET

GOVERNOR

OUTPUT SHAFT

REAR OIL PUMP

REVERSE BAND

OIL STRAINER

KICKDOWN BAND

FRONT OIL PUMP

OVERRUNNING CLUTCHES

Fig. 18 Cutaway of Powerflite transmission

Delayed Shift from Neutral to Drive

1. Kickdown band adjustment.
2. Kickdown band, lever, strut, etc.
3. Oil level too low.

Runaway on Upshifts

1. Oil level too low.
2. Throttle linkage adjustment.
3. Regulator valve or spring.
4. Valve body mating surface leaks.
5. Throttle valve, cam, spring.
6. Kickdown piston, guide, etc.
7. Regulator body mating surfaces leak.
8. Reaction shaft seal.
9. Input shaft seal rings.
10. Reaction shaft bore.
11. Clutch retainer bushing.
12. Clutch shaft seal rings.
13. Clutch discs, plates.
14. Clutch piston, seal rings.
15. Clutch check valve ball.

Runaway on Upshifts Light Throttle Only

1. Front pump worn.

Harsh Upshifts

1. Throttle linkage adjustment.
2. Regulator valve, spring.
3. Valve body mating surface leaks.
4. Manual valve, lever.
5. Kickdown piston, guide, etc.
6. Regulator body mating surfaces leak.
7. Direct clutch spring.
8. Clutch spring retainer snap ring.

Harsh Lift Foot Shifts

1. Throttle linkage adjustment.
2. Valve body mating surface leaks.
3. Throttle valve, cam, spring.
4. Servo pressure bleed valve.
5. Shuttle valve, plug, etc.

Runaway on Downshifts at Part Throttle

1. Oil level low.
2. Gearshift linkage adjustment.
3. Throttle linkage adjustment.
4. Valve body mating surface leaks.
5. Manual valve, lever.
6. Servo restrictor valve.

Harsh Downshift

1. Throttle linkage adjustment.
2. Valve body mating surface leaks.
3. Throttle valve, cam, spring.
4. Servo restrictor valve.
5. Clutch discs, plates.
6. Clutch piston, seal rings.
7. Thrust washers worn.

Runaway on Kickdowns

1. Kickdown band adjustment.
2. Regulator valve, spring.
3. Valve body mating surface leaks.
4. Servo restrictor valve.
5. Shuttle valve, plug, etc.
6. Kickdown piston, guide, etc.
7. Governor assembly.
8. Rear pump assembly.

Harsh Kickdowns

1. Kickdown band adjustment.
2. Regulator valve, spring.

3. Servo pressure bleed valve.
4. Shuttle valve, plug, etc.
5. Kickdown piston, guide, etc.
6. Regulator body mating surfaces leak.
7. Reaction shaft seal.
8. Governor assembly.
9. Rear pump assembly.
10. Input shaft seal rings.
11. Reaction shaft bore.
12. Direct clutch spring.
13. Clutch spring retainer snap ring.
14. Clutch disc, plates.
15. Clutch piston, seal rings.

Shudder During Shifts

1. Shift valve or spring.

IMPROPER RESPONSE TO SHIFT LEVER POSITION

Engine Starts in All Ranges

1. Throttle valve cam on valve body out of adjustment.

No Detent Feel

1. Manual valve or lever.

Detent Not with Pointer

1. Gearshift linkage adjustment.
2. Manual valve or lever.

Gate Not with Pointer

1. Gearshift linkage adjustment.
2. Kickdown band adjustment.
3. Valve body mating surface leaks.
4. Shift valve or spring.

5. Kickdown piston, guide, etc.
6. Regulator body mating surfaces leak.
7. Reaction shaft seal.
8. Input shaft seal rings.
9. Reaction shaft bore.

Moves Forward in Neutral

1. Clutch spring retainer snap ring.
2. Clutch discs or plates.

Moves Forward in Neutral at High Engine Speeds

1. Clutch check valve ball.

Moves Backward in Neutral

1. Gearshift linkage adjustment.
2. Manual valve or lever.
3. Reverse band adjustment.
4. Reverse piston, sleeve, etc.
5. Reverse band, lever, strut, etc.
6. Output shaft support.

No Drive

1. Oil level low.
2. Gearshift linkage adjustment.
3. Regulator valve or spring.
4. Oil strainer clogged.
5. Manual valve or lever.
6. Front pump drive sleeve.
7. Front pump pinion.
8. Front pump assembly worn.
9. Regulator body mating surfaces leak.
10. Planet pinion shafts.
11. Output shaft support.
12. Converter one-way clutch slipping.
13. Defective stator shaft.

No Drive in Drive or Low

1. Throttle valve, cam or spring.
2. Output shaft support.

No Drive in R

1. Pressure checks, line lube, etc.
2. Reverse band adjustment.
3. Reverse servo band or linkage.
4. Broken reverse servo piston ring.

EXCESSIVE SLIP CONDITIONS

Slips in All Ranges

1. Low oil level.
2. Regulator valve or spring.
3. Converter control valve.
4. Valve body mating surface leaks.
5. Front pump drive sleeve.
6. Front pump assembly worn.
7. Regulator body mating surfaces leak.
8. Input shaft seal rings.
9. Reaction shaft bore.

Kickdown Band Slips

1. Throttle linkage adjustment.
2. Kickdown band adjustment.
3. Valve body mating surface leaks.
4. Throttle valve, cam or spring.
5. Valve body end cover plug.
6. Shuttle valve, plug, etc.
7. Kickdown piston, guide, etc.
8. Kickdown band, lever, strut, etc.

Kickdown Band Slips Over 25 MPH

1. Valve body end cover plug.
2. Shuttle valve, plug, etc.

Slips In Drive

1. Valve body mating surface leaks.
2. Kickdown piston, guide, etc.

3. Clutch retainer bushing.
4. Reaction shaft seal rings.
5. Clutch discs or plates.
6. Clutch piston or seal rings.
7. Clutch check valve ball.

Reverse Band Slips

1. Valve body mating surface leaks.
2. Reverse band adjustment.
3. Reverse piston, sleeve, etc.
4. Reverse band, lever, strut, etc.

Slips on Steep Grades

1. Low oil level.

DRAGGING BANDS, CLUTCHES OR BRAKES

Drag in All Ranges

1. Hand brake adjustment.
2. Shift valve or spring.
3. Clutch spring retainer snap ring.

Drag in Drive and Low

1. Reverse band adjustment.
2. Reverse piston, sleeve, etc.
3. Reverse band, lever, strut, etc.
4. Output shaft support.

Drag in Reverse, Drive and Low

1. Valve body mating surface leaks.
2. Regulator body mating surfaces leak.
3. Reaction shaft seal.
4. Input shaft seal rings.
5. Reaction shaft bore.
6. Clutch discs or plates.
7. Clutch piston or seal rings.

Drag in Drive Only

1. Valve body mating surface leaks.
2. Kickdown sun gear snap ring.

Drag in Reverse and Drive

1. Kickdown piston, guide, etc.

ABNORMAL SHIFT PATTERNS

No Upshift

1. Low oil level.
2. Gearshift linkage adjustment.
3. Valve body mating surface leaks.
4. Manual valve or lever.
5. Shift valve or spring.
6. Kickdown piston, guide, etc.
7. Governor assembly.
8. Rear pump assembly.
9. Clutch check valve ball.

Upshift Pattern Low

1. Throttle linkage adjustment.
2. Valve body mating surface leaks.
3. Throttle valve, cam or spring.
4. Shift valve or spring.
5. Governor assembly.
6. Rear pump assembly.

Upshift Pattern Low at Heavy Throttle Only

1. Regulator valve or spring.

All Upshifts 10–15 MPH

1. Throttle valve, cam or spring.
2. Throttle pressure check ball.

Upshift Pattern High

1. Throttle linkage adjustment.
2. Valve body mating surface leaks.
3. Throttle valve, cam or spring.
4. Shift valve or spring.
5. Governor assembly.
6. Rear pump assembly.

Shifts Erratically

1. Low oil level.
2. Valve body mating surface leaks.
3. Shift valve or spring.
4. Output shaft support gaskets.

No Downshift

1. Shift valve or spring.
2. Governor assembly.

Low Downshift Speed

1. Shift valve or spring.

High Downshift Speed

1. Gearshift linkage adjustment.
2. Leaks at valve body mating surface.
3. Manual valve or lever.
4. Kickdown valve ball or rod.

Kickdown at Part Throttle

1. Gearshift linkage adjustment.
2. Leaks at valve body mating surface.
3. Manual valve or lever.
4. Kickdown valve ball or rod.

No Kickdown

1. Throttle linkage adjustment.
2. Leaks at valve body mating surface.
3. Throttle valve, cam or spring.

4. Kickdown valve ball or rod.
5. Shift valve or spring.

Kickdown Limit Low

1. Regulator valve or spring.
2. Leaks at valve body mating surface.
3. Governor assembly.
4. Rear pump assembly.

OTHER DIFFICULTIES

Accelerator Pedal Sticks at Closed Throttle

1. Throttle linkage adjustment.
2. Throttle valve, cam or spring.

Hard to Fill Transmission

1. Breather restricted.
2. Output shaft support gaskets.

Oil Foams from Filler

1. Oil level.
2. Breather restricted.
3. Output shaft support gaskets leak.

Oil Leaks at Seals

1. Breather.
2. External seals.
3. Output shaft support gaskets.

Transmission Overheats

1. Kickdown band adjustment.
2. Converter control valve.
3. Reverse band adjustment.
4. Reverse piston, sleeve, etc.
5. Reverse band, lever, strut, etc.
6. Regulator body mating surfaces leak.
7. Reaction shaft seal.

8. Rear pump assembly.
9. Input shaft seal rings.
10. Reaction shaft bore.
11. Plugged lubrication holes.
12. Kickdown sun gear snap ring.
13. Clutch spring retainer snap ring.
14. Clutch disc or plates.
15. Thrust washers worn.

Impossible to Start Engine by Pushing

1. Output shaft support gaskets leak.
2. Rear pump assembly.

NOISES

Grating Noise with Car Moving

1. Defective speedometer pinion.
2. Rear bearing or snap ring.

Buzzing

1. Oil level.
2. Regulator body mating surfaces leak.

Squealing After Installing Transmission

1. Front pump drive sleeve.
2. Front pump pinion.

Whistling in All Ranges

1. Converter control valve.
2. Front pump drive sleeve.

Rubbing

1. Worn front pump.
2. Thrust washers worn.

Rubbing in Drive Only

1. Kickdown sun gear snap ring.

Excessive Gear Noise

1. Rear pump assembly.
2. Kickdown carrier bushing.
3. Planet pinion shafts.
4. Output shaft support or bushing.

Grinding

1. Oil collector rings.

▶ TORQUEFLITE WITH ALUMINUM CASE, Fig. 19

Harsh Engagement in D-1-2-R

1. Engine idle speed too high.
2. Hydraulic pressures too high or too low.
3. Low-reverse band out of adjustment.
4. Accumulator sticking, broken rings or spring.
5. Low-reverse servo, band or linkage malfunction.
6. Worn or faulty front and/or rear clutch.
7. Valve body malfunction or leakage.

Delayed Engagement in D-1-2-R

1. Low fluid level.
2. Incorrect manual linkage adjustment (1966–69) or incorrect control cable adjustment (1960–65).
3. Oil filter clogged.
4. Hydraulic pressures too high or low.
5. Valve body malfunction or leakage.
6. Accumulator sticking, broken rings or spring.
7. Clutches or servos sticking or not operating.
8. Faulty front oil pump.
9. Worn or faulty front and/or rear clutch.
10. Worn or broken input shaft and/or reaction shaft support seal rings.
11. Aerated fluid.

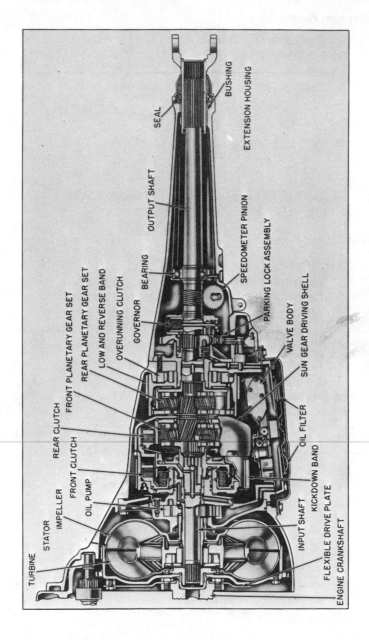

Fig. 19   Cutaway of Torqueflite transmission. Earlier models used a rear pump

Runaway or Harsh Upshift and 3-2 Kickdown

1. Low fluid level.
2. Incorrect throttle linkage adjustment.
3. Hydraulic pressures too high or low.
4. Kickdown band out of adjustment.
5. Valve body malfunction or leakage.
6. Governor malfunction.
7. Accumulator sticking, broken rings or spring.
8. Clutches or servos sticking or not operating.
9. Kickdown servo, band or linkage malfunction.
10. Worn or faulty front clutch.
11. Worn or broken input shaft and/or reaction shaft support seal rings.

No Upshift

1. Low fluid level.
2. Incorrect throttle linkage adjustment.
3. Kickdown band out of adjustment.
4. Hydraulic pressures too high or low.
5. Governor sticking or leaking.
6. Valve body malfunction or leakage.
7. Accumulator sticking, broken rings or spring.
8. Clutches or servos sticking or not operating.
9. Faulty oil pump (1966–69).
10. Faulty rear oil pump (1960–65).
11. Kickdown servo, band or linkage malfunction.
12. Worn or faulty front clutch.
13. Worn or broken input shaft and/or reaction shaft support seal rings.

No Kickdown or Normal Downshift

1. Incorrect throttle linkage adjustment.
2. Incorrect gearshift linkage adjustment (1966–69).
3. Incorrect control cable adjustment (1960–65).
4. Kickdown band out of adjustment.
5. Hydraulic pressure too high or low.
6. Governor sticking or leaking.

7. Valve body malfunction or leakage.
8. Accumulator sticking, broken rings or spring.
9. Clutches or servos sticking or not operating.
10. Kickdown servo, band or linkage malfunction.
11. Overrunning clutch not holding.

Erratic Shifts

1. Low fluid level.
2. Aerated fluid.
3. Incorrect throttle linkage adjustment.
4. Incorrect gearshift control linkage adjustment (1966–69).
5. Incorrect control cable adjustment (1960–65).
6. Hydraulic pressures too high or low.
7. Governor sticking or leaking.
8. Oil filter clogged.
9. Valve body malfunction or leakage.
10. Clutches or servos sticking or not operating.
11. Faulty oil pump (1966–69).
12. Faulty front and/or rear oil pump (1960–65).
13. Worn or broken input shaft and/or reaction shaft support seal rings.

Slips in Forward Drive Positions

1. Low oil level.
2. Aerated fluid.
3. Incorrect throttle linkage adjustment.
4. Incorrect gearshift control linkage adjustment (1966–69).
5. Incorrect control cable adjustment (1960–65).
6. Hydraulic pressures too low.
7. Valve body malfunction or leakage.
8. Accumulator sticking, broken rings or spring.
9. Clutches or servos sticking or not operating.
10. Worn or faulty front and/or rear clutch.
11. Overrunning clutch not holding.
12. Worn or broken input shaft and/or reaction shaft support seal rings.

Slips in Reverse Only

1. Low fluid level.
2. Aerated fluid.
3. Incorrect gearshift control linkage adjustment (1966–69).
4. Incorrect control cable adjustment (1960–65).
5. Hydraulic pressures too high or low.
6. Low-reverse band out of adjustment.
7. Valve body malfunction or leakage.
8. Front clutch or rear servo sticking or not operating.
9. Low-reverse servo, band or linkage malfunction.
10. Faulty oil pump (front on 1960–65).

Slips in All Positions

1. Low fluid level.
2. Hydraulic pressures too low.
3. Valve body malfunction or leakage.
4. Faulty oil pump (front on 1960–65).
5. Clutches or servos sticking or not operating.
6. Worn or broken input shaft and/or reaction shaft support seal rings.

No Drive in Any Position

1. Low fluid level.
2. Hydraulic pressures too low.
3. Oil filter clogged.
4. Valve body malfunction or leakage.
5. Faulty oil pump (front on 1960–65).
6. Clutches or servos sticking or not operating.
7. Torque converter failure.

No Drive in Forward Drive Positions

1. Hydraulic pressures too low.
2. Valve body malfunction or leakage.
3. Accumulator sticking, broken rings or spring.

4. Clutches or servos, sticking or not operating.
5. Worn or faulty rear clutch.
6. Overrunning clutch not holding.
7. Worn or broken input shaft and/or reaction shaft support seal rings.

No Drive in Reverse

1. Incorrect gearshift control linkage adjustment (1966–69).
2. Incorrect control cable adjustment (1960–65).
3. Hydraulic pressures too low.
4. Low-reverse band out of adjustment.
5. Valve body malfunction or leakage.
6. Front clutch or rear servo sticking or not operating.
7. Low-reverse servo, band or linkage malfunction.
8. Worn or faulty front clutch.

Drives in Neutral

1. Incorrect gearshift control linkage adjustment (1966–69).
2. Incorrect control cable adjustment (1960–65).
3. Valve body malfunction or leakage.
4. Rear clutch inoperative.

Drags or Locks

1. Kickdown band out of adjustment.
2. Low-reverse band out of adjustment.
3. Kickdown and/or low-reverse servo, band or linkage malfunction.
4. Front and/or rear clutch faulty.
5. Planetary gear sets broken or seized.
6. Overrunning clutch worn, broken or seized.

Grating, Scraping or Growling Noise

1. Kickdown band out of adjustment.
2. Low-reverse band out of adjustment.
3. Output shaft bearing and/or bushing damaged.

4. Governor support binding or broken seal rings.
5. Oil pump scored or binding (either pump on 1960–65).
6. Front and/or rear clutch faulty.
7. Planetary gear sets broken or seized.
8. Overrunning clutch worn, broken or seized.

Buzzing Noise

1. Low fluid level.
2. Pump sucking air (both pumps on 1960–65).
3. Valve body malfunction.
4. Overrunning clutch inner race damaged.

Hard to Fill, Oil Flows Out Filler Tube

1. High fluid level.
2. Breather clogged.
3. Oil filter clogged.
4. Aerated fluid.

Transmission Overheats

1. Low fluid level.
2. Kickdown band adjustment too tight
3. Low-reverse band adjustment too tight.
4. Faulty cooling system.
5. Cracked or restricted oil cooler line or fitting.
6. Faulty oil pump (either pump on 1960–65).
7. Insufficient clutch plate clearance in front and/or rear clutches.

Starter Will Not Energize in Neutral or Park

1. Incorrect gearshift control linkage adjustment (1966–69).
2. Incorrect control cable adjustment (1960–65).
3. Faulty or incorrectly adjusted neutral starting switch.
4. Broken lead to neutral switch.

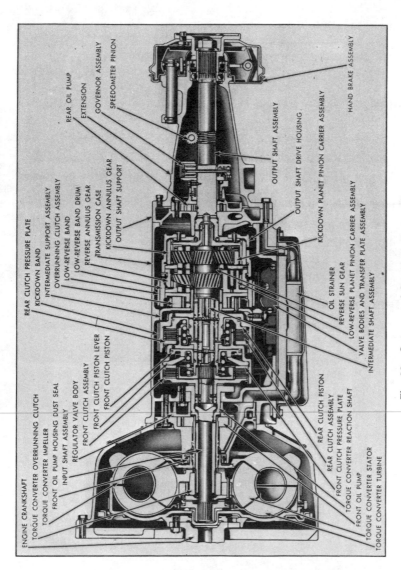

ENGINE CRANKSHAFT
TORQUE CONVERTER OVERRUNNING CLUTCH
TORQUE CONVERTER IMPELLER
FRONT OIL PUMP HOUSING DUST SEAL
INPUT SHAFT ASSEMBLY
REGULATOR VALVE BODY
FRONT CLUTCH ASSEMBLY
FRONT CLUTCH PISTON LEVER
FRONT CLUTCH PISTON

REAR CLUTCH PRESSURE PLATE
KICKDOWN BAND
INTERMEDIATE SUPPORT ASSEMBLY
OVERRUNNING CLUTCH ASSEMBLY
LOW-REVERSE BAND
LOW-REVERSE BAND DRUM
REVERSE ANNULUS GEAR
TRANSMISSION CASE
KICKDOWN ANNULUS GEAR
OUTPUT SHAFT SUPPORT

REAR OIL PUMP
EXTENSION
GOVERNOR ASSEMBLY
SPEEDOMETER PINION

OUTPUT SHAFT ASSEMBLY

OUTPUT SHAFT DRIVE HOUSING

HAND BRAKE ASSEMBLY

KICKDOWN PLANET PINION CARRIER ASSEMBLY

OIL STRAINER
REVERSE SUN GEAR
LOW-REVERSE PLANET PINION CARRIER ASSEMBLY
VALVE BODIES AND TRANSFER PLATE ASSEMBLY
INTERMEDIATE SHAFT ASSEMBLY

REAR CLUTCH PISTON
REAR CLUTCH ASSEMBLY
REAR CLUTCH PRESSURE PLATE
FRONT CLUTCH PRESSURE PLATE
TORQUE CONVERTER REACTION SHAFT
FRONT OIL PUMP
TORQUE CONVERTER STATOR
TORQUE CONVERTER TURBINE

Fig. 20   Cutaway of Cast Iron Torqueflite

Impossible to Push Start, 1960–65 Only

1. Low fluid level.
2. Low-reverse band slipping.
3. Valve body malfunction or leakage.
4. Rear oil pump faulty.
5. Low-reverse servo, band or linkage malfunction.
6. Worn or faulty rear clutch.
7. Worn or broken input shaft and/or reaction shaft support seal rings.

▶ TORQUEFLITE WITH CAST IRON CASE, Fig. 20

SHIFT DIFFICULTIES

Harsh N to D or N to R

1. Pressure checks, line lube, etc.
2. Low-reverse band adjustment.
3. Engine idle.
4. L-R servo band or linkage.
5. Accumulator.
6. Front clutch.
7. Rear clutch.

Delayed N to D

1. Oil level.
2. Pressure checks, line lube, etc.
3. Valve body—bolts, mating surfaces.
4. Accumulator.
5. Air pressure check.
6. Front pump.
7. Front clutch.

Runaway on Upshift & 3-2 Kickdown

1. Oil level.
2. Throttle linkage adjustment.
3. Pressure checks, line lube, etc.

4. Kickdown band adjustment.
5. Kickdown servo band or linkage.
6. Valve body—bolts, mating surfaces.
7. Accumulator.
8. Air pressure check.
9. Rear clutch.

Harsh Upshift & 3-2 Kickdown

1. Throttle linkage adjustment.
2. Pressure checks, line lube, etc.
3. Kickdown band adjustment.
4. Kickdown servo band or linkage.
5. Valve body—bolts, mating surfaces.
6. Accumulator.
7. Rear clutch.

No Upshift

1. Oil level.
2. Throttle linkage adjustment.
3. Pressure checks, line lube, etc.
4. Kickdown band adjustment.
5. Kickdown servo band or linkage.
6. Valve body—bolts, mating surfaces.
7. Accumulator.
8. Air pressure check.
9. Governor.
10. Rear clutch.

No Kickdown or Normal Downshift

1. Oil level.
2. Throttle linkage adjustment.
3. Gearshift control cable adjustment.
4. Pressure checks, line lube, etc.
5. Kickdown band adjustment.
6. Kickdown servo band or linkage.
7. Valve body—bolts, mating surfaces.
8. Accumulator.

9. Air pressure check.
10. Governor.
11. Overrunning clutch.

Shifts Erratically

1. Oil level.
2. Throttle linkage adjustment.
3. Gearshift control cable adjustment.
4. Pressure checks, line lube, etc.
5. Engine idle.
6. Regulator valve or spring.
7. Output shaft rear bearing.
8. Oil strainer.
9. Valve body—bolts, mating surfaces.
10. Air pressure check.
11. Governor.
12. Front pump—drive sleeve.

OPERATING DIFFICULTIES

Slips in Forward Drive Position

1. Oil level.
2. Pressure checks, line lube, etc.
3. Valve body—bolts, mating surfaces.
4. Accumulator.
5. Air pressure check.
6. Regulator valve body, gasket, mating surfaces.
7. Front clutch.
8. Rear clutch.
9. Overrunning clutch.

Slips in L-R Only

1. Pressure checks, line lube, etc.
2. Low-reverse band adjustment.
3. Low-reverse servo band or linkage.
4. Valve body—bolts, mating surfaces.
5. Air pressure check.
6. Regulator valve body, gasket, mating surfaces.

Slips in All Positions

1. Oil level.
2. Pressure checks, line lube, etc.
3. Regulator valve or spring.
4. Valve body—bolts, mating surfaces.
5. Air pressure check.
6. Front pump.
7. Regulator valve body, gasket, mating surfaces.

No Drive in Any Position

1. Oil level.
2. Pressure checks, line lube, etc.
3. Regulator valve or spring.
4. Oil strainer.
5. Valve body—bolts, mating surfaces.
6. Air pressure check.
7. Front pump.
8. Regulator valve body, gasket, mating surfaces.
9. Converter one-way clutch slipping.
10. Defective stator shaft.

No Drive in Forward Ranges

1. Pressure checks, line lube, etc.
2. Kickdown band adjustment.
3. Kickdown servo band or linkage.
4. Valve body—bolts, mating surfaces.
5. Accumulator.
6. Air pressure check.
7. Front clutch.
8. Rear clutch.
9. Overrunning clutch.

No Drive in R

1. Pressure checks, line lube, etc.
2. Low-reverse band adjustment.
3. Low-reverse servo band or linkage.

4. Air pressure check.
5. Rear clutch.
6. Stuck reverse blocker valve (one piece valve body).
7. Broken reverse servo piston ring.

Drives in N

1. Gearshift control cable adjustment.
2. Valve body—bolts, mating surfaces.
3. Front clutch.

MISCELLANEOUS

Drags or Locks

1. Kickdown band adjustment.
2. Low-reverse band adjustment.
3. Hand brake adjustment.
4. Kickdown servo band on linkage.
5. Low-reverse servo band or linkage.
6. Front clutch.
7. Rear clutch.
8. Planetary gear set.
9. Overrunning clutch.

Grating, Scraping Noise

1. Hand brake adjustment.
2. Output shaft rear bearing.
3. Governor.
4. Rear pump.
5. Front pump.
6. Front clutch.
7. Rear clutch.
8. Planetary gear set.

Buzzing Noises

1. Oil level.
2. Regulator valve or spring.

   3. Converter control valve.
   4. Regulator valve body, gasket, mating surfaces.

Trans. Hard to Fill—Oil Blows Out Fill Tube

   1. Oil level.
   2. Regulator valve or spring.
   3. Converter control valve.
   4. Breather.
   5. Oil strainer.
   6. Front pump.
   7. Regulator valve body, gasket, mating surfaces.

Transmission Overheats

   1. Oil level.
   2. Kickdown band adjustment.
   3. Low-reverse band adjustment.
   4. Hand brake adjustment.
   5. Regulator valve or spring.
   6. Converter control valve.
   7. Torque converter cooling.
   8. Rear pump.
   9. Front pump.
  10. Regulator valve body, gasket, mating surfaces.
  11. Front clutch.
  12. Rear clutch.

Impossible to Push

   1. Oil level.
   2. Pressure checks, line lube, etc.
   3. Low-reverse band adjustment.
   4. Low-reverse servo band or linkage.
   5. Valve body—bolts, mating surfaces.
   6. Rear pump.

Starter Won't Energize

   1. Gearshift control cable adjustment.
   2. Starting switches.

▶ FORD AUTOMATIC TRANSMISSIONS
C4 TRANSMISSION, Fig. 21

Rough Initial Engagement in D, D2, 2, D1

1. Engine idle speed.
2. Vacuum diaphgragm unit or tubes restricted, leaking or maladjusted.
3. Check control pressure.
4. Pressure regulator.
5. Valve body.
6. Forward clutch.

1-2 or 2-3 Shift Points Erratic

1. Check fluid level.
2. Vacuum diaphragm unit or tubes restricted, leaking or maladjusted.
3. Intermediate servo.
4. Manual linkage adjustment.
5. Governor.
6. Check control pressure.
7. Valve body.
8. Make air pressure check.

Rough 1-2 Upshifts

1. Vacuum diaphragm unit or tubes restricted, leaking or maladjusted.
2. Intermediate servo.
3. Intermediate band.
4. Check control pressure.
5. Valve body.
6. Pressure regulator.

Rough 2-3 Upshifts

1. Vacuum diaphragm unit or tubes restricted, leaking or maladjusted.
2. Intermediate servo.
3. Check control pressure.

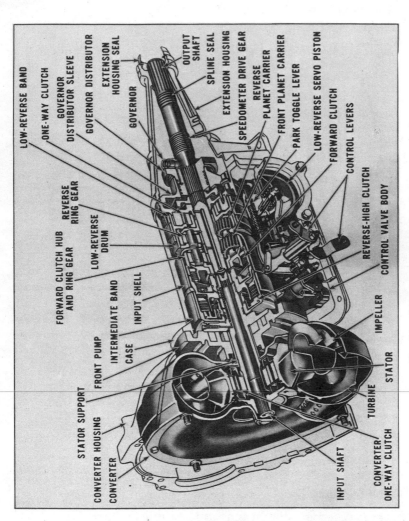

Fig. 21 Cutaway of C4 transmission

4. Pressure regulator.
5. Intermediate band.
6. Valve body.
7. Make air pressure check.
8. Reverse-high clutch.
9. Reverse-high clutch piston air bleed valve.

Dragged Out 1-2 Shift

1. Check fluid level.
2. Vacuum diaphragm unit or tubes restricted, leaking or maladjusted.
3. Intermediate servo.
4. Check control pressure.
5. Intermediate band.
6. Valve body.
7. Pressure regulator.
8. Make air pressure check
9. Leakage in hydraulic system.

Engine Overspeeds on 2-3 Shift

1. Manual linkage.
2. Check fluid level.
3. Vacuum diaphragm unit or tubes restricted, leaking or maladjusted.
4. Reverse servo.
5. Check control pressure.
6. Valve body.
7. Pressure regulator.
8. Intermediate band.
9. Reverse-high clutch.
10. Reverse-high clutch piston air bleed valve.

No 1-2 or 2-3 Shift

1. Manual linkage.
2. Downshift linkage, including inner lever position.
3. Vacuum diaphragm unit or tubes restricted, leaking or maladjusted.

4. Governor.
5. Check control pressure.
6. Valve body.
7. Intermediate band.
8. Intermediate servo.
9. Reverse-high clutch.
10. Reverse-high clutch piston air bleed valve.

No 3-1 Shift in D1 or 2 or 3-2 Shift in D or D2

1. Governor.
2. Valve body.

No Forced Downshifts

1. Downshift linkage, including inner lever position.
2. Valve body.
3. Vacuum diaphragm unit or tubes restricted, leaking or maladjusted.

Runaway Engine on Forced 3-2 Downshift

1. Check control pressure.
2. Intermediate servo.
3. Intermediate band.
4. Pressure regulator.
5. Valve body.
6. Vacuum diaphragm unit or tubes restricted, leaking or maladjusted.
7. Leakage in hydraulic system.

Rough 3-2 or 3-1 Shift at Closed Throttle

1. Engine idle speed.
2. Vacuum diaphragm unit or tubes restricted, leaking or maladjusted.
3. Intermediate servo.
4. Valve body.
5. Pressure regulator.

Shifts 1-3 in Either D Position

1. Intermediate band.
2. Intermediate servo.
3. Vacuum diaphragm unit or tubes restricted, leaking or maladjusted.
4. Valve body.
5. Governor.
6. Make air pressure check.

No Engine Braking in 1st Gear—Manual Low

1. Manual linkage.
2. Reverse band.
3. Reverse servo.
4. Valve body.
5. Governor.
6. Make air pressure check.

Slips or Chatters in 1st Gear—Drive Right

1. Check fluid level.
2. Vacuum diaphragm unit or tubes restricted, leaking or maladjusted.
3. Check control pressure.
4. Pressure regulator.
5. Valve body.
6. Forward clutch.
7. Leakage in hydraulic system.
8. Planetary one-way clutch.

Slips or Chatters in 2nd Gear

1. Check fluid level.
2. Vacuum diaphragm unit or tubes restricted, leaking or maladjusted.
3. Intermediate servo.
4. Intermediate band.
5. Check control pressure.
6. Pressure regulator.
7. Valve body.

8. Make air pressure check.
9. Forward clutch.
10. Leakage in hydraulic system.

Slips or Chatters in R

1. Check fluid level.
2. Vacuum diaphragm unit or tubes restricted, leaking or maladjusted.
3. Reverse band.
4. Check control pressure.
5. Reverse servo.
6. Pressure regulator.
7. Valve body.
8. Make air pressure check.
9. Reverse-high clutch.
10. Leakage in hydraulic system.
11. Reverse-high piston air bleed valve.

No Drive in Drive Right Only

1. Check fluid level.
2. Manual linkage.
3. Check control pressure.
4. Valve body.
5. Make air pressure check.
6. Planetary one-way clutch.

No Drive in Drive Left Only

1. Check fluid level.
2. Manual linkage.
3. Check control pressure.
4. Intermediate servo.
5. Valve body.
6. Make air pressure check.
7. Leakage in hydraulic system.
8. Planetary one-way clutch.

No Drive in L or 1 Only

1. Check fluid level.
2. Manual linkage.
3. Check control pressure.
4. Valve body.
5. Reverse servo.
6. Make air pressure check.
7. Leakage in hydraulic system.
8. Planetary one-way clutch.

No Drive in R Only

1. Check fluid level.
2. Manual linkage.
3. Reverse band.
4. Check control pressure.
5. Reverse servo.
6. Valve body.
7. Make air pressure check.
8. Reverse-high clutch.
9. Leakage in hydraulic system.
10. Reverse-high clutch piston air bleed valve.

No Drive in Any Selector Position

1. Check fluid level.
2. Manual linkage.
3. Check control pressure.
4. Pressure regulator.
5. Valve body.
6. Make air pressure check.
7. Leakage in hydraulic system.
8. Front pump.

Lockup in Drive Right Only

1. Reverse-high clutch.
2. Parking linkage.
3. Leakage in hydraulic system.

Lockup in Drive Left Only

1. Reverse band.
2. Reverse servo.
3. Reverse-high clutch.
4. Parking linkage.
5. Leakage in hydraulic system.
6. Planetary one-way clutch.

Lockup in L Only

1. Intermediate band.
2. Intermediate servo.
3. Reverse-high clutch.
4. Parking linkage.
5. Leakage in hydraulic system.

Lockup in R Only

1. Intermediate band.
2. Intermediate servo.
3. Forward clutch.
4. Parking linkage.
5. Leakage in hydraulic system.

Parking Lock Binds or Does Not Hold

1. Manual linkage.
2. Parking linkage.

Maximum Speed Too Low, Poor Acceleration

1. Engine performance.
2. Brakes bind.
3. Converter one-way clutch.

Noisy in N or P

1. Check fluid level.
2. Pressure regulator.
3. Front pump.
4. Planetary assembly.

Noisy in All Gears

1. Check fluid level.
2. Pressure regulator.
3. Planetary assembly.
4. Forward clutch.
5. Front pump.
6. Planetary one-way clutch.

Car Moves Forward in N

1. Manual linkage.
2. Forward clutch.

▶ FORD C6 TRANSMISSION, Fig. 22

No Drive in Forward Ranges

1. Manual linkage adjustment.
2. Check control pressure.
3. Valve body.
4. Make air pressure check.
5. Forward clutch.
6. Leakage in hydraulic system.

Rough Initial Engagement in D, D1, D2 or 2

1. Engine idle speed too high.
2. Vacuum diaphragm unit or tubes restricted, leaking or maladjusted.
3. Check control pressure.
4. Valve body.
5. Forward clutch.

1-2 or 2-3 Shift Points Incorrect or Erratic

1. Check fluid level.
2. Vacuum diaphragm unit or tubes restricted, leaking or maladjusted.
3. Downshift linkage, including inner lever position.
4. Manual linkage adjustment.
5. Governor defective.

6. Check control pressure.
7. Valve body.
8. Make air pressure check.

Rough 1-2 Upshifts

1. Vacuum diaphragm unit or tubes restricted, leaking or maladjusted.
2. Intermediate servo.
3. Intermediate band.
4. Check control pressure.
5. Valve body.

Rough 2-3 Shifts

1. Vacuum diaphragm or tubes restricted, leaking or maladjusted.
2. Intermediate servo.
3. Check control pressure.
4. Intermediate band.
5. Valve body.
6. Make air pressure check.
7. Reverse-high clutch.
8. Reverse-high clutch piston air bleed valve.

Dragged Out 1-2 Shift

1. Check fluid level.
2. Vacuum diaphragm unit or tubes restricted, leaking or maladjusted.
3. Intermediate servo.
4. Check control pressure.
5. Intermediate band.
6. Valve body.
7. Make air pressure check.
8. Leakage in hydraulic system.

Engine Overspeeds on 2-3 Shift

1. Manual linkage adjustment.
2. Check fluid level.

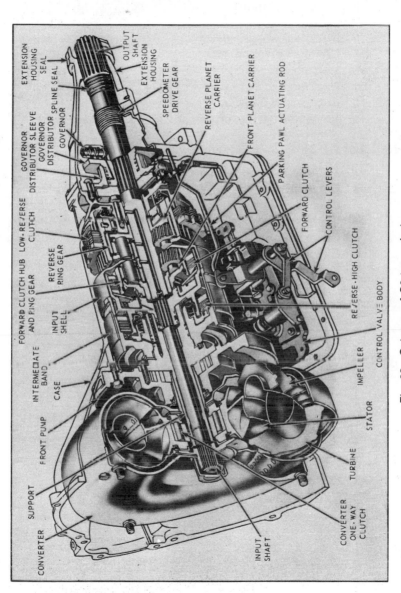

Fig. 22 Cutaway of C6 transmission

3. Vacuum diaphragm unit or tubes restricted, leaking or maladjusted.
4. Intermediate servo.
5. Check control pressure.
6. Valve body.
7. Intermediate band.
8. Reverse-high clutch.
9. Reverse-high clutch piston air bleed valve.

No 1-2 or 2-3 Shift

1. Manual linkage adjustment.
2. Downshift linkage including inner lever position.
3. Vacuum diaphragm unit or tubes restricted, leaking or maladjusted.
4. Governor.
5. Check control pressure.
6. Valve body.
7. Intermediate band.
8. Intermediate servo.
9. Reverse-high clutch.
10. Leakage in hydraulic system.

No 3-1 Shift in D1, 2 or 3-2 Shift in D2, D

1. Governor.
2. Valve body.

No Forced Downshifts

1. Downshift linkage, including inner lever position.
2. Check control pressure.
3. Valve body.

Runaway Engine on Forced 3-2 Shift

1. Check control pressure.
2. Intermediate servo.
3. Intermediate band.
4. Valve body.

5. Vacuum diaphragm unit or tubes restricted, leaking or maladjusted.
6. Leakage in hydraulic system.

Rough 3-2 Shift or 3-1 Shift at Closed Throttle

1. Engine idle speed.
2. Vacuum diaphragm unit or tubes restricted, leaking or maladjusted.
3. Intermediate servo.
4. Check control pressure.
5. Valve body.

Shifts 1-3 in D1, D2, D, 2

1. Intermediate band.
2. Intermediate servo.
3. Valve body.
4. Governor.
5. Make air pressure check.

No Engine Braking in 1st Gear—Manual Low Range

1. Manual linkage adjustment.
2. Low-reverse clutch.
3. Valve body.
4. Governor.
5. Make air pressure check.
6. Leakage in hydraulic system.

Creeps Excessively

1. Engine idle speed too high.

Slips or Chatters in 1st, D1 or 2

1. Check fluid level.
2. Vacuum diaphragm unit or tubes restricted, leaking or maladjusted.
3. Check control pressure.
4. Valve body.
5. Forward clutch.

6. Leakage in hydraulic system.
7. Planetary one-way clutch.

Slips or Chatters in 2nd Gear

1. Check fluid level.
2. Vacuum diaphragm unit or tubes restricted, leaking or maladjusted.
3. Intermediate servo.
4. Intermediate band.
5. Check control pressure.
6. Valve body.
7. Make air pressure check.
8. Forward clutch.
9. Leakage in hydraulic system.

Slips or Chatters in Reverse

1. Check fluid level.
2. Vacuum diaphragm unit or tubes restricted, leaking or maladjusted.
3. Manual linkage adjustment.
4. Low-reverse clutch.
5. Check control pressure.
6. Valve body.
7. Make air pressure check.
8. Reverse-high clutch.
9. Leakage in hydraulic system.
10. Reverse-high clutch piston air bleed valve.

No Drive in D1 or 2

1. Manual linkage adjustment.
2. Check control pressure.
3. Valve body.
4. Planetary one-way clutch.

No Drive in D2 or D

1. Check fluid level.
2. Manual linkage adjustment.
3. Check control pressure.

4. Intermediate servo.
5. Valve body.
6. Make air pressure check.
7. Leakage in hydraulic system.

No Drive in L or 1

1. Check fluid level.
2. Check control pressure.
3. Valve body.
4. Make air pressure check.
5. Leakage in hydraulic system.

No Drive in R Only

1. Check fluid level.
2. Manual linkage adjustment.
3. Low-reverse clutch.
4. Check control pressure.
5. Valve body.
6. Make air pressure check.
7. Reverse-high clutch.
8. Leakage in hydraulic system.
9. Reverse-high clutch piston air bleed valve.

No Drive in Any Selector Position

1. Check fluid level.
2. Manual linkage adjustment.
3. Check control pressure.
4. Valve body.
5. Make air pressure check.
6. Leakage in hydraulic system.
7. Front pump.

Lockup in D1 or 2

1. Valve body.
2. Parking linkage.
3. Leakage in hydraulic system.

Lockup in D2 or D

1. Low-reverse clutch.
2. Valve body.
3. Reverse-high clutch.
4. Parking linkage.
5. Leakage in hydraulic system.
6. Planetary one-way clutch.

Lockup in L or 1

1. Valve body.
2. Parking linkage.
3. Leakage in hydraulic system.

Lockup in R Only

1. Valve body.
2. Forward clutch.
3. Parking linkage.
4. Leakage in hydraulic system.

Parking Lock Binds or Does Not Hold

1. Manual linkage adjustment.
2. Parking linkage.

Transmission Overheats

1. Oil cooler and connections.
2. Valve body.
3. Vacuum diaphragm unit or tubes restricted, leaking or maladjusted.
4. Check control pressure.
5. Converter one-way clutch.
6. Converter pressure check valves.

Maximum Speed Too Low, Poor Acceleration

1. Engine performance.

2. Car brakes.
3. Forward clutch.

Transmission Noisy in N and P

1. Check fluid level.
2. Valve body.
3. Front pump.

Noisy in 1st, 2nd, 3rd or Reverse

1. Check fluid level.
2. Valve body.
3. Planetary assembly.
4. Forward clutch.
5. Reverse-high clutch.
6. Planetary one-way clutch.

Fluid Leak

1. Check fluid level.
2. Converter drain plugs.
3. Oil pan gasket, filler tube or seal.
4. Oil cooler and connections.
5. Manual or downshift lever shaft seal.
6. ⅛″ pipe plugs in case.
7. Extension housing-to-case gasket.
8. Extension housing rear oil seal.
9. Speedometer driven gear adapter seal.
10. Vacuum diaphragm unit or tubes.
11. Intermediate servo.
12. Engine rear oil seal.
13. Front pump oil seal.
14. Front pump-to-case gasket or seal.

Car Moves Forward in N

1. Manual linkage adjustment.
2. Forward clutch.

▶ FoMoCo THREE SPEED AUTOMATIC TRANSMISSIONS, Fig. 23

Rough Initial Engagement

1. Idle speed.
2. Vacuum unit or tubes, 1961–69.
3. Throttle linkage, 1959–60.
4. Rear band, 1959–60.
5. Front band, 1961–69.
6. Check control pressure.
7. Pressure regulator.
8. Valve body.

Shift Points High, Low or Erratic

1. Fluid level.
2. Vacuum unit or tubes, 1961–69.
3. Throttle linkage, 1959–60.
4. Manual linkage.
5. Governor.
6. Check control pressure.
7. Valve body.
8. Inner and outer throttle levers 1959–60.
9. Downshift linkage, 1961–69.

Rough 2-3 Shift

1. Throttle linkage, 1959–60.
2. Manual linkage, 1961–69.
3. Front band.
4. Vacuum unit or tubes, 1961–69.
5. Pressure regulator.
6. Valve body.
7. Front servo.

Engine Overspeeds, 2-3 Shift

1. Vacuum unit or tubes, 1961–69.
2. Throttle linkage, 1959–60.

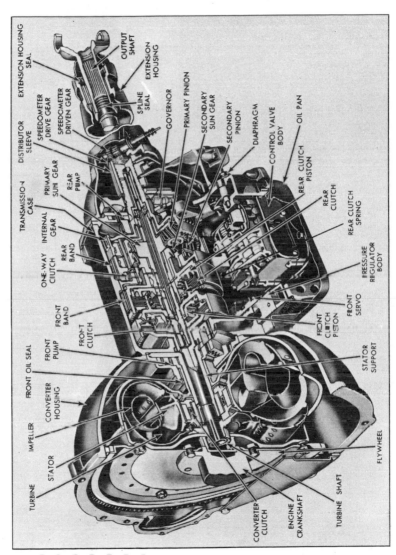

Fig. 23 Cutaway of Ford 3 Speed (cast iron case)

3. Front band.
4. Valve body.
5. Pressure regulator, 1961–69.

No 1-2 or 2-3 Shifts

1. Governor.
2. Valve body.
3. Manual linkage, 1961–69.
4. Rear clutch.
5. Front band, 1961–69.
6. Front servo, 1961–69.
7. Leakage in hydraulic system.
8. Fluid distributor sleeve in output shaft, 1959–60.
9. Pressure regulator, 1961–69.

No Forced Downshifts

1. Throttle linkage, 1959–60.
2. Downshift linkage, 1961–69.
3. Check control pressure.
4. Valve body.
5. Inner and outer throttle levers, 1959–60.

Rough 3-2 or 3-1 Shifts

1. Engine idle speed.
2. Vacuum unit or tubes, 1961–69.
3. Throttle linkage, 1959–60.
4. Valve body.

Slips or Chatters in 2nd

1. Fluid level.
2. Vacuum unit or tubes, 1961–69.
3. Throttle linkage, 1959–60.
4. Front band.
5. Check control pressure.
6. Pressure regulator.
7. Valve body.
8. Front servo.

9. Front clutch.
10. Leakage in hydraulic system.

Slips or Chatters in 1st

1. Fluid level.
2. Vacuum unit or tubes, 1961–69.
3. Throttle linkage, 1959–60.
4. Rear band, 1959–60.
5. Check control pressure.
6. Pressure regulator.
7. Valve body.
8. Inner and outer throttle levers, 1959–60.
9. Front clutch.
10. Leakage in hydraulic system.
11. Fluid distributor sleeve in output shaft.
12. Planetary one-way clutch.

Slips or Chatters in Reverse

1. Fluid level.
2. Throttle linkage, 1959–60.
3. Rear band.
4. Check control pressure.
5. Pressure regulator.
6. Valve body.
7. Rear servo, 1961–69.
8. Rear clutch.
9. Vacuum unit or tubes, 1961–69.
10. Leakage in hydraulic system.
11. Fluid distributor sleeve in output shaft.

No Drive in D Ranges

1. Front band, 1959–60.
2. Valve body.
3. Make air pressure check.
4. Manual linkage, 1961–69.
5. Front clutch.
6. Leak in hydraulic system.
7. Fluid distributor sleeve in output shaft.

No Drive in D1 or D

1. Manual linkage.
2. Valve body.
3. Planetary one-way clutch.

No Drive in L or 1

1. Manual linkage.
2. Rear band, 1959–60.
3. Front clutch, 1961–69.
4. Rear servo, 1959–60.
5. Valve body.
6. Make air pressure check.
7. Leak in hydraulic system.
8. Fluid distributor sleeve in output shaft.

No Drive in R

1. Rear band.
2. Rear servo.
3. Valve body.
4. Make air pressure check.
5. Rear clutch.
6. Leak in hydraulic system.
7. Fluid distributor sleeve in output shaft.

No Drive in Any Range

1. Fluid level.
2. Manual linkage.
3. Check control pressure.
4. Pressure regulator.
5. Valve body.
6. Make air pressure check.
7. Leak in hydraulic system.

Lockup in D, D1, D2 or 2

1. Manual linkage.
2. Rear band, 1959–60.

3. Rear servo.
4. Front servo.
5. Rear clutch.
6. Parking linkage.
7. Leak in hydraulic system.

Lockup in D2 or D

1. Manual linkage.
2. Rear band.
3. Rear servo.
4. Rear clutch.
5. Parking linkage.
6. Leak in hydraulic system.
7. Planetary one-way clutch.

Lockup in R

1. Front band.
2. Front servo.
3. Front clutch.
4. Parking linkage.
5. Leak in hydraulic system.

Lockup in L or 1

1. Front band.
2. Pressure regulator, 1961–69.
3. Front servo, 1959–60.
4. Valve body.
5. Rear clutch.
6. Parking linkage.
7. Leak in hydraulic system.

Parking Lock Binds or Won't Hold

1. Manual linkage.
2. Parking linkage.

Unable to Push Start

1. Fluid level.
2. Manual linkage.

   3. Pressure regulator.
   4. Valve body.
   5. Rear pump.
   6. Leak in hydraulic system.

Transmission Overheats

   1. Converter cooling air passages, 1959–60.
   2. Oil cooler and connections.
   3. Pressure regulator.
   4. Converter one-way clutch.

Engine Runaway on Forced Downshift

   1. Front band.
   2. Pressure regulator.
   3. Valve body.
   4. Front servo.
   5. Vacuum unit or tubes, 1961–69.
   6. Leak in hydraulic system.

Maximum Speed Below Normal, Acceleration Poor

   1. Converter one-way clutch.

No 2-1 Downshift 1959-60

   1. Throttle linkage.
   2. Valve body.
   3. Rear servo.

No 3-1 Downshift

   1. Engine idle speed.
   2. Vacuum unit or tubes, 1961–69.
   3. Throttle linkage, 1959–60.
   4. Valve body.

Noise in Neutral

   1. Pressure regulator.
   2. Engine rear oil seal, 1959–60.

3. Front clutch.
4. Front pump.

Noise in 1-2-3 or R

1. Pressure regulator.
2. Planetary assembly.
3. Front clutch.
4. Rear clutch.
5. Front pump.

Noise In Reverse

1. Pressure regulator.
2. Front pump.

Noise on Coast in Neutral

1. Rear pump.

▶ FoMoCo TWO SPEED AUTOMATIC TRANSMISSIONS, Fig. 24

Harsh Initial Engagement in D, L and R

1. Engine idle speed.
2. Vacuum unit or tube leaking.
3. Throttle linkage.
4. Check control pressure.

Slips or Chatters in D or L

1. Fluid level.
2. Check control pressure.
3. Control valve body.
4. Low band adjustment.
5. Make air pressure check.
6. Leakage in low servo apply circuit.
7. Engine-transmission mounts.

8. Low servo and band.
9. Planetary gears.

Car Won't Move in D but Will in L

1. Low servo piston check valve.

Slips or Chatters in R

1. Fluid level.
2. Check control pressure.
3. Manual linkage.
4. Control valve body.
5. Reverse band adjustment.
6. Air pressure check.
7. Leakage in reverse servo apply circuit.
8. Engine-transmission mounts.
9. Reverse servo and band.
10. Cracked or broken rear band anchor.

Engine Overspeeds During 1-2 Shift

1. Fluid level.
2. Check for burned clutch plates if there is fluid odor.
3. Check control pressure.
4. Low band adjustment.
5. Air pressure check.
6. Control valve body.
7. Leakage in clutch apply or low servo release circuit.
8. High clutch.

Momentary Lock-Up During 1-2 Shift

1. Fluid level.
2. Control pressure check.
3. Control valve body.
4. Low band adjustment.
5. Low servo and band.
6. High clutch.
7. Low servo piston return spring.

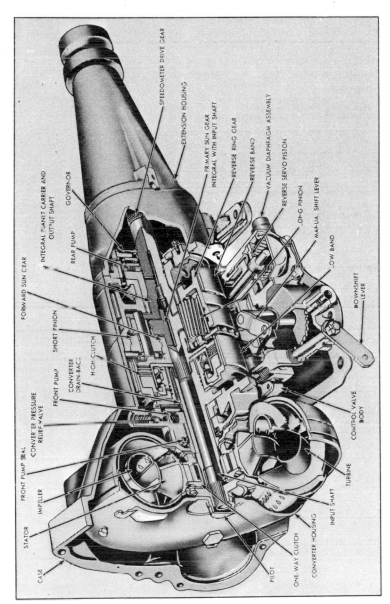

Fig. 24 Cutaway of Ford 2 Speed with vacuum controlled throttle valve

Severe 2-1 Shift During Coast-Down

1. Engine idle speed.
2. Throttle linkage.
3. Control valve body.
4. Control pressure check.
5. Low band adjustment.

No 1-2 Shift in D

1. Fluid level.
2. Check for burned clutch plates if there is fluid odor.
3. Manual linkage.
4. Governor.
5. High clutch piston.
6. Low servo and band.
7. Leakage in control pressure main circuit.
8. High clutch.
9. High clutch piston.
10. Rear pump.

Delayed or Severe 1-2 Shift

1. Vacuum diaphragm or tube leakage.
2. Throttle linkage.
3. Governor.
4. Control valve body.
5. Leakage in control pressure main circuit.
6. Low servo piston check valve.

Slips Continuously After 1-2 Shift

1. Check for burned clutch plates if there is fluid odor.
2. Fluid level.
3. Check control pressure.
4. Air pressure check.
5. Control valve body.
6. High clutch.
7. Leakage in clutch apply or low servo release circuit.

No 2-1 Forced Downshift

1. Downshift linkage.
2. Control valve body.
3. Leakage in control pressure main circuit.

No 2-1 Shift During Coast-Down

1. Control valve body.
2. Governor.

Fluid Forced Out Vent

1. Fluid level.
2. Transmission external vent.
3. Fluid aeration.
4. Fluid contaminated with engine coolant.
5. Cooler flow check.

Transmission Overheats

1. Fluid level.
2. Control pressure check.
3. Converter cooler air passages.
4. Cooler flow check.
5. Converter one-way clutch.
6. Fluid check for engine coolant contamination.
7. Transmission external vent.

Acceleration Normal—Maximum Speed About 50 mph

1. Converter one-way clutch.

Acceleration Poor—Operation Above 30 mph Normal with Steady Throttle

1. Converter one-way clutch.

Engine Won't Push Start

1. Fluid level.
2. Manual linkage.
3. Control valve body.
4. Low band adjustment.

5. Low servo piston check valve.
6. Rear pump.
7. Leakage in control pressure main circuit.
8. Low servo and band.
9. Leakage in low servo apply circuit.

Parking Lock Doesn't Hold or Binds

1. Manual linkage.
2. Parking linkage.
3. Front band installed backwards—strut out of position.

▶ WARNER AUTOMATIC TRANS RAMBLER & "J" SERIES JEEP & SCOUT

Harsh Engagement

1. Front clutch seized or plates distorted.
2. Rear clutch seized or plates distorted.

Delayed Forward Engagement

1. Sealing rings missing or broken.
2. Front clutch piston check valve leaks.

Delayed Reverse Engagement

1. Sealing rings missing or broken.

No Engagement

1. Sealing rings missing or broken.
2. Broken input shaft.
3. Front pump drive tangs or converter hub broken.
4. Front pump worn.
5. Defective converter.

No Forward D-1

1. Sealing rings missing or broken.
2. Front clutch slipping, worn plates or faulty parts.

3. One-way (sprag) clutch slipping or incorrectly installed.
4. Front clutch piston check valve leaks.

No Forward D-2

1. Sealing rings missing or broken.
2. Front clutch slipping, worn plates or faulty parts.
3. Front clutch piston check valve leaks.

No Reverse

1. Sealing rings missing or broken.
2. Rear clutch slipping, worn or faulty parts.
3. Rear band worn or broken.

No Neutral

1. Front clutch seized or distorted plates.

No 1-2 Upshift

1. Sealing rings missing or broken.
2. Output shaft plug missing (6 cyl.).

No 2-3 Upshift

1. Sealing rings missing or broken.
2. Rear clutch slipping, worn or faulty parts.
3. Rear clutch piston ball check leaks.
4. Output shaft plug missing (6 cyl.).

Shift Points Too High

1. Sealing rings missing or broken.

Shift Points Too Low

1. Sealing rings missing or broken.

1-2 Delayed Followed Close By 2-3 Shift

1. Sealing rings missing or broken.
2. Front clutch slipping, worn plates or faulty parts.
3. Front band worn or broken.

2-3 Slips

1. Sealing rings missing or broken.
2. Rear clutch slipping, worn or faulty parts.
3. Front band worn or broken.
4. Rear clutch pistol ball check leaks.

Harsh 1-2 Shift

1. Front clutch slipping, worn plates or faulty parts.

Harsh 2-3 Shift

1. Rear clutch seized or plates distorted.

1-2 Ties Up

1. Rear clutch seized or plates distorted.
2. One-way (sprag) clutch seized.

No 2-1 in D-1

1. One-way (sprag) clutch slipping or incorrectly installed.
2. Output shaft plug missing (6 cyl.).

No 2-1 in L Range

1. Rear band worn or broken.
2. Output shaft plug missing (6 cyl.).

No 3-2 Shift

1. Front band worn or broken.
2. Output shaft plug missing (6 cyl.).

Shift Points Too High or Too Low

1. Sealing rings missing or broken.

2-1 Slips

1. Front clutch slipping, worn plates or faulty parts.
2. Front pump drive tangs or converter hub broken.
3. Front clutch piston check valve leaks.

3-2 Slips

1. Sealing rings missing or broken.
2. Rear clutch slipping, worn or faulty parts.
3. Front band worn or broken.
4. Rear clutch piston ball check leaks.

Harsh 2-1 Shift

1. Sealing rings missing or broken.
2. Front clutch slipping, worn plates or faulty parts.
3. One-way (sprag) clutch slipping or incorrectly installed.

Harsh 3-2 Shift

1. Rear clutch slipping, worn or faulty parts.
2. Rear clutch seized or plates distorted.

Clips or Chatters in Reverse

1. Sealing rings missing or broken.
2. Front clutch seized or plates distorted.
3. Rear clutch slipping, worn or faulty parts.
4. Rear band worn or broken.
5. Rear clutch piston ball check leaks.

Reverse Tie Up

1. Sealing rings missing or broken.
2. Front clutch seized or plates distorted.

Low Idle Pressure

1. Sealing rings missing or broken.
2. Front pump worn.

Low Stall Pressure

1. Sealing rings missing or broken.
2. Front pump worn.
3. Output shaft plug missing (6 cyl.).

Stall Speed Too Low

1. Converter.

Stall Speed Too High D-1

1. Broken output shaft.
2. Broken gears.
3. Sealing rings missing or broken.
4. Front clutch slipping, worn plates or faulty parts.
5. One-way (sprag) clutch slipping or incorrectly installed.
6. Broken input shaft.
7. Converter.
8. Front clutch piston check valve leaks.

Reverse Too High

1. Broken output shaft.
2. Broken gears.
3. Rear band worn or broken.
4. Rear clutch slipping, worn or faulty parts.
5. Broken input shaft.
6. Converter.

Poor Acceleration

1. Output shaft plug missing (6 cyl.).
2. Converter.

Noisy in Neutral

1. Rear clutch seized or plates distorted.
2. Front pump.
3. Front clutch hub thrust washer missing (detectable in N, P, R only).
4. Converter.

Noisy in Park

1. Front pump.
2. Front clutch hub thrust washer missing (detectable in N, P, R only).
3. Converter.

Noisy in All Gears

1. Front pump.
2. Planetary assembly.
3. Converter.

Noisy in 1st & 2nd Gears Only

1. Front pump.
2. Planetary assembly.
3. Forward sun gear thrust washer missing.

Park Brake Does Not Hold

1. Parking linkage.

Oil Out Breather

1. Sealing rings missing or broken.
2. Breather baffle missing.

Oil Out Fill Tube

1. Sealing rings missing or broken.
2. Breather baffle missing

Ties Up in L or D-1, 1st Gear

1. Rear clutch seized or plates distorted.
2. Sealing rings missing or broken.

Ties Up in D-1 or D-2, 2nd & 3rd Gears

1. Rear clutch seized or plates distorted.
2. Sealing rings missing or broken.
3. One-way (sprag) clutch seized.

Chatters D-1, D-2 or Low

1. Sealing rings missing or broken.
2. Front clutch slipping, worn plates or faulty parts.
3. Front clutch piston check valve leaks.

▶ VOLKSWAGEN AUTOMATIC

No Drive in Any Range

1. Low oil level.
2. Oil pump or drive defective.
3. Shafts or planet gear set broken.
4. Drive plate broken.

No Drive in Any Forward Range

1. Forward clutch defective.

No Drive with Lever in 1 or Reverse

1. 1st and Reverse band or servo faulty.

No Drive in 1st Gear with Lever in 3 Position

1. 1st gear one-way clutch in annulus gear defective.

No Drive in 2nd Gear with Lever in 2 or 3 Position

1. 2nd gear band or servo faulty.

No Drive in 3rd or Reverse

1. Direct and reverse clutch faulty.

No Upshift Out of 1st Gear

1. Governor drive defective.
2. Governor valve sticking.

Power Transmission Erratic

1. Low oil level.
2. Selector lever incorrectly adjusted.

Delayed Engagement, Engine Races

1. Oil level incorrect.
2. Friction linings burnt or worn.
3. Oil pressure wrong due to incorrect adjustment of vacuum unit.
4. Incorrect oil pressure due to internal leakage.

Shifts Occur When Speed is Too Low

1. Defective governor.
2. Defective valve body.
3. Misadjusted vacuum unit.
4. Leakage in transmission.

Shifts Occur When Speed is Too High

1. Vacuum unit or hose leaking.
2. Defective valve body.
3. Defective governor.
4. Misadjusted vacuum unit.
5. Leakage in transmission.

No Upshift To 3rd

1. Incorrect governor pressure.
2. Defective valve body.
3. Direct and reverse clutch defective.

Harsh Engagement when Lever is Shifted into Gear

1. Idle speed too high.
2. Vacuum hose leaking.

Vehicle Creeps

1. Idle speed too high.

No Kickdown

1. Incorrect throttle linkage and switch adjustment.
2. Electrical fault in kickdown circuit.
3. Valve body defective or dirty.

Poor Acceleration; Low Maximum Speed

1. Faulty converter.
2. Bands or clutches slipping.
3. Low oil level.

Poor Acceleration; Screeching Noise When Moving Off

1. Converter or one-way clutch faulty. Make stall test to check.

Oil Consumption Without External Leakage

1. Vacuum unit leaking.
2. Oil seals on pinion or governor shaft faulty (oil getting into final drive housing).

Parking Lock Not Working

1. Incorrect selector lever adjustment.
2. Operating linkage broken.

▶ REAR AXLE TROUBLES

Noise When Pulling Straight Ahead

1. Not enough oil.
2. Wrong grade of oil.
3. Poor quality oil.
4. Ring gear and pinion have excessive backlash.
5. Ring gear and pinion worn.
6. Pinion shaft bearings worn or loose.
7. Pinion shaft end play excessive.
8. Ring gear and pinion misaligned because of bent axle housing or distorted differential case.
9. Ring gear warped.
10. Differential bearings worn or loose.
11. Ring gear rivets or screws loose.
12. Ring gear and pinion not matched set.

Noise When Coasting in Gear

Any axle noise which is heard when the engine is pulling the car is likely to be heard when coasting although not as loud as when pulling.

If ring gear and pinion are meshed too tight, the noise will be greater when decelerating. The noise will disappear when the engine is pulling unless the gears are very tight.

Excessive end play of pinion shaft due to loose pinion nut or incorrect adjustment.

Intermittent Noise

1. Warped ring gear.
2. Loose ring gear rivets or screws.
3. Ring gear improperly installed on differential case due to dirt or burrs between the two.

Knocks or Clicks

1. Flat spot on ring gear or pinion tooth, or tooth chipped, or particle of metal lodged on tooth.
2. Flat spot on bearing.
3. Loose axle shaft key.
4. Loose splined shafts.
5. Mis-matched differential case halves.

Noise on Turns

1. Differential pinions or side gears chipped, scuffed or teeth broken.
2. Differential pinions binding on pinion shaft.
3. Differential pinions or side gears loose due to worn bushings or shaft.
4. Excessive backlash between pinions and side gears.
5. Excessive axle shaft end play.
6. Contacting surfaces between side gear and differential case burred, scored or otherwise damaged.

Oil Leaks at Axle Ends

1. Oil level too high.
2. Oil too light or poor quality.
3. Axle shaft oil seals worn.
4. Axle shaft bearing retainer loose.
5. Cracked rear axle housing.
6. Vent (if any) clogged.

Oil Leak at Pinion Shaft

1. Oil level too high.
2. Oil too light or poor quality.
3. Pinion oil seal worn.

4. Pinion oil seal retainer distorted, loose in housing or improperly installed.
5. Oil return passage in carrier housing restricted.
6. Universal joint companion flange hub rough, scored or out of round.
7. Universal joint companion flange loose on pinion shaft.

▶ DRUM BRAKE TROUBLES

One Brake Drags

1. Brake line restricted.
2. Improperly adjusted or worn wheel bearing.
3. Distorted or improperly adjusted brake shoe.
4. Faulty retracting spring.
5. Drum out of round.
6. Loose backing plate.
7. Faulty wheel cylinder.
8. Dirty brake fluid.
9. Air in hydraulic system.
10. Insufficient shoe-to-backing plate lubrication.

All Brakes Drag

1. Mechanical resistance at pedal or shoes; damaged linkage.
2. Brake line restricted.
3. Distorted or improperly adjusted brake shoes.
4. Dirty brake fluid.
5. Faulty master cylinder.
6. Sticking booster control valve.

Hard Pedal

1. Mechanical resistance at pedal or shoes; damaged linkage.
2. Brake line restricted.
3. Distorted or improperly adjusted brake shoes.

4. Linings glazed or worn.
5. Oil or grease in lining.

Spongy Pedal

1. Leaks or insufficient fluid.
2. Air in hydraulic system.

Car Pulls to One Side

1. Brake line restricted.
2. Improper tire pressure.
3. Improperly adjusted or worn wheel bearing.
4. Distorted or improperly adjusted brake shoes.
5. Faulty retracting spring.
6. Drum out of round.
7. Linings glazed or worn.
8. Oil or grease in lining.
9. Loose lining.
10. Faulty wheel cylinder.
11. Self-adjusters not operating.

One Wheel Locks

1. Distorted or improperly adjusted brake shoes.
2. Linings glazed or worn.
3. Oil or grease in lining.
4. Loose backing plate.
5. Faulty wheel cylinder.
6. Tire tread worn.

Brakes Chatter

1. Drum out of round.
2. Linings glazed or worn.
3. Oil or grease in lining.
4. Loose backing plate.
5. Loose lining.
6. Poor lining-to-drum contact.
7. Loose front suspension.

Excessive Pedal Travel

1. Leaks or insufficient fluid.
2. Distorted or improperly adjusted brake shoes.
3. Linings glazed or worn.
4. Faulty master cylinder.
5. Air in hydraulic system.
6. Self-adjusters not operating.
7. Cracked drum.

Pedal Gradually Goes to Floor

1. Leaks or insufficient fluid.
2. Faulty master cylinder.

Brakes Uneven

1. Improper tire pressure.
2. Oil or grease in lining.
3. Scored drum.
4. Dirty brake fluid.

Shoe Click Release

1. Self-adjusters not operating.
2. Insufficient shoe-to-backing plate lubrication.
3. "Threads" left by drum turning tool pull shoes sideways.

Noisy or Grabbing Brakes

1. Distorted or improperly adjusted brake shoes.
2. Linings glazed or worn.
3. Oil or grease in lining.
4. Scored drum.
5. Dirt on drum-lining surface.
6. Faulty wheel cylinder.
7. Sticking booster control valve.

Brakes Do Not Apply

1. Leaks or insufficient fluid.
2. Linings glazed or worn.

3. Oil or grease in lining.
4. Dirty brake fluid.
5. Faulty master cylinder.
6. Air in hydraulic system.

▶ DISC BRAKE TROUBLES

Excessive Pedal Travel

1. Shoe and lining knock back after violent cornering or rough road travel.
2. Piston and shoe and lining assembly not properly seated or positioned.
3. Air leak or insufficient fluid in system or caliper.
4. Loose wheel bearing adjustment.
5. Damaged or worn caliper piston seal.
6. Improper booster push rod adjustment.
7. Shoe out of flat more than .005".
8. Rear brake automatic adjusters inoperative.
9. Improperly ground rear brake shoe and lining assemblies.

Brake Roughness or Chatter; Pedal Pumping

1. Excessive lateral run-out of rotor.
2. Rotor excessively out of parallel.

Excessive Pedal Effort

1. Frozen or seized pistons.
2. Brake fluid, or grease on linings.
3. Shoe and lining worn below specifications.
4. Proportioning valve malfunction.
5. Booster inoperative.
6. Leaking booster vacuum check valve.

Pull, Uneven or Grabbing Brakes

1. Frozen or seized pistons.
2. Brake fluid, oil or grease on linings.
3. Caliper out of alignment with rotor.

4. Loose caliper attachment.
5. Unequalized front tire pressure.
6. Incorrect front end alignment.
7. Lining protruding beyond end of shoe.

Brake Rattle

1. Excessive clearance between shoe and caliper or between shoe and splash shield.
2. Shoe hold-down clips missing or improperly positioned.

Heavy Brake Drag

1. Frozen or seized pistons.
2. Operator riding brake pedal.
3. Incomplete brake pedal return due to linkage interference.
4. Faulty booster check valve holding pressure in hydraulic system.
5. Residual pressure in front brake hydraulic system.

Caliper Brake Fluid Leak

1. Damaged or worn caliper piston seal.
2. Scores in cylinder bore.
3. Corrosion build-up in cylinder bore or on piston surface.
4. Metal clip in seal groove.

No Braking Effect When Pedal is Depressed

1. Piston and shoe and lining assembly not properly seated or positioned.
2. Air leak or insufficient fluid in system or caliper.
3. Damaged or worn caliper piston seal.
4. Bleeder screw open.
5. Air in hydraulic system or improper bleeding.

▶ POWER BRAKE TROUBLES

Trouble Diagnosis

To tell whether the power system is operating at all, stop the engine and apply the brakes several times to exhaust vacuum reserve. Now depress the brake pedal and, while maintaining light pressure on the pedal, start engine. If the power system is operating, the pedal will tend to move forward and less effort will be required to keep brakes applied.

If the power system is not operating first check the vacuum supply as a possible cause. Start the engine and bring it up to medium speed. Turn off ignition and immediately close throttle to increase manifold vacuum. Wait at least 90 seconds, then try the brakes. If there is insufficient reserve for three or more power applications, the vacuum check valve is faulty or there is a leak or obstruction in the power cylinder, reserve tank or lines.

When the vacuum supply is adequate, failure of the system to supply the proper assist is to be found in the power unit itself.

Don't forget that some of the troubles listed may be in the brakes themselves, rather than in the power unit. A hard pedal may be due to swollen wheel or master cylinder cups, or to a defective or kinked flexible hydraulic line. Grabbing can be caused by grease or hydraulic fluid on the lining; drag from misadjustment; a spongy pedal from air in the lines.

To pinpoint the source of vacuum leakage connect a vacuum gauge to a "T" fitting inserted between the power unit and reserve tank. Start the engine and read the vacuum at slow idle. Shut off the engine. With the system in good condition, the reading will be maintained on the gauge for at least 15 seconds. If it drops, there is leakage.

To find the point of leakage, disconnect the line to the reserve tank and plug that end of the "T" fitting. Then repeat the test. If the reading is now maintained for at least 15 seconds the reserve tank is leaking. If the reading still drops, the leak is in the power cylinder or check valve.

To determine which, insert the "T" into a vacuum line running direct from the check valve to the reserve tank. This disconnects the power cylinder. Repeat the test. If the gauge drops, there is leakage past the check valve. If it now holds the reading, the leakage is in the power cylinder. Not all cars are equipped with reserve tanks but the same method of eliminating one unit at a time can be used in making the test on any car.

The cause of power brake problems in general as they apply to the different makes and types of power units are as follows:

Bendix Diaphragm Type

Hard Pedal or No Assist—Air cleaner element clogged, control valve faulty, defective diaphragm, worn or distorted reaction plate or levers, cracked or broken power piston or levers, internal or external leaks.

Brakes Grab—Control valve defective or sticking, bind in linkage, reaction diaphragm leaking, worn or distorted levers or plate.

No or Slow Release—Push rod adjustment incorrect, linkage binding, return spring defective.

Bendix Hydrovac

Hard Pedal—Internal or external vacuum or hydraulic leak, low fluid level, control valve defective.

Brakes Grab—Sticky control valve, power piston sticking, sticking ball check in hydraulic piston in slave cylinder chamber.

No or Slow Release—Internal friction, sluggish control valve.

Brake Pedal Chatter—Residual check valve defective.

Brakes Apply When Engine Is Started—Control valve piston sticking, atmospheric poppet return spring defective.

Bendix Treadle-Vac, Reaction Type

Hard Pedal—Internal vacuum hose loose or restricted, jammed vacuum cylinder plate screws, faulty piston seal.

Brake Grab—Counter reaction spring broken, poppet valve sticking.

Slow or No Release—Air passages restricted, hydraulic seal friction excessive, compensating valve or valve plunger sticking, poppet valve stuck in closed position.

Bendix Power-Vac

Hard Pedal—Blocked air cleaner element.

Slow Release—Pedal trigger arm improperly adjusted.

Bendix Master-Vac

Hard Pedal—Internal vacuum hose loose or restricted, jammed vacuum cylinder piston, vacuum leaks from loose piston screws, faulty piston seal, leak between power and master cylinders, control valve jammed.

Brakes Grab—Counter reaction spring broken, sticking poppet valve.

Slow or No Release—Piston return spring broken, valve plunger sticking, air passage restricted, piston stroke interference.

Bendix Piston Type

Hard Pedal—Internal vacuum hose loose or restricted, jammed vacuum cylinder piston, vacuum leaks from loose piston plate screws, faulty piston seal, leak between power and master cylinders, control valve jammed.

Brakes Grab—Counter reaction spring broken, sticking poppet valves.

Slow or No Release—Piston return spring broken, valve plunger sticking, air passage restricted, piston stroke interference.

Delco-Moraine Air Suspended Diaphragm Type

Hard Pedal—Vacuum hose in unit loose or restricted, restricted air cleaner, internal vacuum leak, jammed sliding valve.

Brakes Grab—Floating valve diaphragm leakage due to faulty rubber bumper pad in valve, improper number of shims on air valve.

Slow or No Release—Broken vacuum piston return spring, restricted air cleaner, bent or dented vacuum cylinder.

Delco-Moraine, Piston Type

Hard Pedal—Vacuum hose in unit loose or restricted, restricted air cleaner, internal vacuum leak, jammed sliding valve.

Brakes Grab—Floating valve diaphragm leakage due to faulty rubber bumper pad in valve, improper number of shims on air valve.

Slow or No Release—Broken vacuum piston return spring, restricted air cleaner, bent or dented vacuum cylinder.

Delco-Moraine Vacuum Suspended Diaphragm Type, 1959–61

Hard Pedal—Internal vacuum hose loose or restricted, jammed air valve, vacuum leak in unit, defective diaphragm, restricted air cleaner, badly distorted reaction plate or levers.

Brakes Grab—Reaction diaphragm leaks or passage restricted, valve sticking, dislodged reaction levers, broken reaction spring, faulty control valve.

Slow or No Release—Blocked air passage, air cleaner blocked, broken piston return spring, broken air valve spring.

Delco-Moraine Vacuum Suspended Diaphragm Type, 1962–70

Hard Pedal—Internal vacuum leak, faulty control valve.

Brakes Grab—Faulty control valve.

Slow or No Release—Faulty push rod adjustment, bind in linkage.

Kelsey-Hayes Diaphragm Type

Hard Pedal—Faulty vacuum check valve, vacuum hose or pipe collapsed, plugged, kinked or disconnected, internal leaks, vacuum leaks in unit caused by improper assembly, missing parts, damaged parts or foreign matter, cups swollen by improper fluid, improper push rod adjustment, badly dented vacuum cylinder, bound up pedal linkage, improperly adjusted stop light switch, scored valve plunger, broken or missing springs.

Brakes Grab—Faulty pedal linkage, dented vacuum cylinder, sticking control piston, defective vacuum check valve, loose vacuum connections.

Kelsey-Hayes Oval Bellows Type

Hard Pedal—Blocked air passage in piston guide sleeve assembly or in air cleaner element, inspection screw or gasket loose or missing, vacuum passage blocked in valve housing, vacuum valve binding in guide due to defective spring or dry seal, valve operating rod binding.

Brakes Grab—Seals binding.

Slow or No Release—Push rod incorrectly adjusted, guide sleeve bearing seal binding on sleeve.

Brake Pedal Chatter—Power brake trigger bent or out of adjustment, trigger pivot rubber collar defective, guide sleeve bearing seal binding on sleeve, pedal push rod incorrectly adjusted.

Kelsey-Hayes Round Bellows Type

Hard Pedal—Valve eccentric or push rod incorrectly adjusted, bent pedal trigger.

Brake Pedal Chatter—Valve eccentric or push rod incorrectly adjusted.

No or Slow Release—Clogged air filter, incorrcetly adjusted push rod.

Midland-Ross Diaphragm Type

Hard Pedal—Leak in bellows, diaphragm assembly out of place in housing.

Brakes Grab—Sticking actuating valve assembly.

Brakes Drag—Sticking valve plunger.

Brakes Self-Apply When Engine Is Started—Leak in rear housing, diaphragm out of position in housing allowing air into rear chamber, sticking or unseated air valve.

▶ FRONT END & STEERING TROUBLES

Hard Steering

1. Low or uneven tire pressure.
2. Steering gear or connections adjusted too tight.
3. Insufficient or incorrect lubricant used.
4. Excessive caster.
5. Suspension arms bent or twisted.
6. Front spring sagged.
7. Frame bent or broken.
8. Steering knuckle bent.
9. Kingpin galled or frozen in bushing.
10. Excessive steering shaft coupling misalignment.

Excessive Play or Looseness in Steering

1. Steering gear connections adjusted too loose or worn.
2. Steering knuckle bushings worn.
3. Front wheel bearings incorrectly adjusted or worn.
4. Worn ball joints.
5. Worn or loose worm steering shaft bearings.
6. Worn control arm bushings.

Rattle or Chuckle in Steering Gear

1. Insufficient or improper lubricant in steering gear.
2. Excessive backlash in steering gear.
3. Worn or loose worm steering shaft bearings.
4. Pitman arm loose on shaft.

Erratic Steering on Application of Brakes

1. Oil or brake fluid on lining.
2. Brakes improperly adjusted.
3. Front spring weak.

4. Low or uneven tire pressure.
5. Insufficient or uneven caster.
6. Steering knuckle bent.

Car Pulls to One Side

1. Low or uneven tire pressure.
2. Incorrect or uneven caster or camber.
3. Wheel bearings adjusted too tight.
4. Uneven front car height.
5. Toe-in incorrect.
6. Oil or brake fluid on brake lining.
7. Brakes incorrectly or unevenly adjusted.
8. Steering knuckle or knuckle support bent.
9. Frame bent or broken.
10. Shock absorbers inoperative.
11. Rear wheels not tracking with front wheels.
12. Rear axle shifted (spring U bolts loose or center bolt sheared).
13. Broken or weak rear springs.

Scuffed Tires

1. Tire improperly inflated
2. Toe-in incorrect.
3. Excessive wheel or tire run-out.
4. Steering knuckle bushings worn.
5. Uneven camber.
6. Incorrect toe-out on turns.
7. Suspension arms bent or twisted.
8. Steering knuckle bent.
9. Excessive speed on turns.

Cupped Tires

1. Improper toe-in.
2. Tires improperly inflated.
3. Wheels, tires or brake drums out of balance.
4. Dragging brakes.
5. Worn steering knuckle bushings.

6. Wheel bearings incorrectly adjusted or worn.
7. Uneven camber.
8. Steering knuckle bent.
9. Excessive mileage without rotating tires.

Front Wheel Shimmy

1. Low or uneven tire pressure.
2. Wheels, tires or brake drums out of balance.
3. Excessive wheel or tire run-out.
4. Shock absorbers inoperative.
5. Steering connections incorrectly adjusted or worn.
6. Steering gear incorrectly adjusted.
7. Front wheel bearings incorrectly adjusted or worn.
8. Incorrect or uneven caster.
9. Steering knuckle bushings worn.
10. Toe-in incorrect.
11. Steering knuckle bent.
12. Eccentric or bulged tires.
13. Stabilizer inoperative.
14. Worn ball joints.
15. Worn control arm bushings.

Front Wheel Tramp

1. Wheels, tires or brake drums out of balance.
2. Wheel or tire not concentric.
3. Shock absorbers inoperative.
4. Stabilizer inoperative.

Car Wanders

1. Low or uneven tire pressure.
2. Steering gear or connections adjusted too loose or worn.
3. Steering gear or connections adjusted too tight.
4. Steering knuckle bushings worn.
5. Improper toe-in.
6. Incorrect or uneven caster or camber.
7. Steering knuckle bent.

8. Kingpin bent.
9. Rear axle shifted (spring U bolts loose or center bolt sheared).
10. Stabilizer inoperative.
11. Kingpins or bushings tight.
12. Bind in lower or upper control arm shaft.
13. Bind in rear spring shackles or dry rear springs.
14. Excessive backlash in steering gear.

Road Shocks

1. High air pressure in tires.
2. Steering gear or connections incorrectly adjusted.
3. Excessive caster.
4. Shock absorbers inoperative.
5. Front springs weak or sagged.
6. Wrong type or size of tires used.
7. Steering knuckle bent.

▶ CHRYSLER CONSTANT CONTROL TYPE

Hard Steering

1. Tires not properly inflated.
2. Low oil level in reservoir.
3. Loose pump belt.
4. Oil on pump belts.
5. Steering linkage needs lubrication.
6. Power steering pump output low.
7. Cross shaft adjustment too tight.
8. Pressure control valve stuck in closed position.
9. External oil leaks.
10. Defective or damaged valve lever.
11. Dirt or chips in steering gear.
12. Damaged column support worm shaft bearings.
13. Damaged thrust bearings or excessive preload adjustment.
14. Rough or hard to turn worm and piston assembly.
15. Excessive internal leakage.

Poor Recovery from Turns

1. Tires not properly inflated.
2. Steering linkage binding.
3. Improper wheel alignment.
4. Damaged or defective steering tube bearings.
5. Steering column jacket and steering gear not properly aligned.
6. Improper cross shaft mesh adjustment.
7. Pressure control valve piston stuck open.
8. Column support spanner nut loose.
9. Defective or damaged valve lever.
10. Improper worm thrust bearing adjustment.
11. Burrs or nicks in reaction ring grooves in cylinder head or column support.
12. Defective or damaged cylinder head worm shaft seal ring.
13. Dirt or chips in steering gear unit.
14. Rough or catchy worm and piston assembly.

Self-Steering or Leads to Either Side

1. Tires not properly inflated.
2. Improper wheel alignment.
3. Steering wheel off center when car is traveling straight ahead.
4. Valve body out of adjustment.
5. Valve lever damaged.
6. Column support spanner nut loose.

Temporary Increase in Effort When Turning Steering Wheel

1. Low oil level.
2. Loose pump belt.
3. Oil on pump belts.
4. Binding steerage linkage.
5. Engine idle too slow.
6. Defective power steering pump.
7. Air in system.
8. External adjustment.

9. Improper cross shaft adjustment.
10. Excessive internal leakage.

Excessive Steering Wheel Free Play

1. Improper cross shaft adjustment.
2. Column support spanner nut loose.
3. Improper worm thrust bearing adjustment.

Lack of Assistance in One Direction

1. Oil leaking past worm shaft cast iron seal ring or ferrule "O" ring.

Lack of Assistance in Both Directions

1. Broken "O" ring on worm piston.
2. Piston end plug loose.
3. Pump belt slipping.
4. Pump output low.

Noises

1. Buzzing noise in neutral only is caused by sticking pressure control valve.
2. Noisy power pump.
3. Damaged hydraulic lines.
4. Pressure control valve sticking.
5. Improper sector shaft adjustment.
6. Air in system.

▶ FORD TORSION BAR TYPE

Hard Steering

1. Low or uneven tire pressure.
2. Improper gear adjustment.
3. Improper wheel alignment.
4. Low fluid level.
5. Twisted or bent suspension parts, frame and linkage components.
6. Tight wheel bearings.

7. Steering spindle bent.
8. Pump belt out of adjustment.
9. Pump output low.
10. Air in system.
11. Valve spool out of adjustment.
12. Valve spool sticking.
13. Steering linkage binding.

Hard Steering Straight Ahead

1. Steering adjustment too tight.
2. Steering gear shaft binding.

Hard Steering While Turning or Parking

1. Oil level low.
2. Pump pressure low.
3. Pressure loss in steering gear due to leakage past "O" rings.
4. Pressure loss between valve spool and sleeve.
5. Pressure loss past piston ring or scored housing bore.

Loose Steering

1. Loose wheel bearings.
2. Loose tie rod ends or linkage.
3. Worn ball joints.
4. Worn suspension parts.
5. Insufficient mesh loads.
6. Insufficient worm bearing preload.
7. Valve spool out of adjustment.

Erratic Steering

1. Oil or brake fluid on brake lining.
2. Out of round brake drums.
3. Improperly adjusted brakes.
4. Under-inflated tires.
5. Broken spring or other details in suspension system.

6. Improper caster adjustment.
7. Fluid level low.

Binding or Poor Recovery

1. Steering gear shaft binding.
2. Steering gear out of adjustment.
3. Steering linkage binding.
4. Valve spool binding due to dirt or burred edges.
5. Valve spool out of adjustment.
6. Interference at sector shaft and ball stud.

Loss of Power Assist

1. Pump inoperative.
2. Hydraulic lines damaged.
3. Power cylinder damaged.
4. Valve spool out of adjustment.

Loss of Power Assist in One Direction

1. Valve spool out of adjustment.

Noisy Pump

1. Air being drawn into pump.
2. Lines touching other parts of car.
3. Oil level low.
4. Excessive back pressure caused by obstructions in lines.
5. Excessive wear of internal parts.

Poor Return of Steering Gear to Center

1. Valve spool sticking.
2. Valve spool out of adjustment.
3. All items given under "Binding or Poor Recovery."

Steering Wheel Surge While Turning

1. Valve spool sticking.
2. Excessive internal leakage.
3. Belt slippage.

▶ SAGINAW ROTARY VALVE TYPE

Hard Steering

1. Frozen steering shaft bearings.
2. Lower coupling flange rubbing against adjuster.
3. Steering adjustment tight.

Poor Return of Steering

1. Frozen steering shaft bearings.
2. Lower coupling flange rubbing against adjuster.
3. Tires not inflated properly.
4. Incorrect caster and toe-in.
5. Tight steering linkage.
6. Steering gear misalignment.
7. Tight suspension ball joints.
8. Steering adjustment tight.
9. Thrust bearing adjustment tight.
10. Tight sector-to-rack piston adjustment.
11. Rack piston nut and worm preload too tight.
12. Sticky valve spool.

Car Leads to One Side

1. Front end misalignment.
2. Unbalanced or badly worn valve.

Momentary Increase in Effort When Turning Wheel Fast

1. Low oil level in pump.
2. Pump belt slipping.
3. High internal leakage.

External Oil Leaks

1. Loose hose connections.
2. Damaged hose.
3. Side cover O-ring seal.
4. Pitman shaft seals.
5. Housing end plug seal.

6. Adjuster plug seals.
7. Torsion bar seal.

Steering Gear Noise

1. A rattle or chuckle noise caused by loose over-center adjustment.
2. A hissing sound caused by gear being loose on frame.

Excessive Wheel Kickback or Loose Steering

1. Lash in steering linkage.
2. Air in system.
3. Excessive lash between pitman shaft sector and rack piston.
4. Loose thrust bearing adjustment.
5. Ball nut and worm preload.

Wheel Surges or Jerks

1. Loose pump belt.

Hard Steering When Parking

1. Loose pump belt.
2. Low oil level in reservoir.
3. Lack of lubrication in linkage or front suspension.
4. Tires not properly inflated.
5. Insufficient oil pressure.
6. Low oil pressure due to restriction in hoses.
7. Low oil pressure due to worn piston ring or scored housing bore.
8. Pressure loss due to leakage at valve rings, valve body-to-worm seal or rack piston end plug seal.
9. Pressure loss due to loose fit of spool in valve body or leaky valve body.

Valve Squawk

1. Cut or worn dampener ring on valve spool.
2. Loose or worn rotary valve parts.

No Effort Required to Turn

1. Broken torsion bar.

▶ POWER TOP, WINDOW & SEAT TROUBLES

HYDRO-LECTRIC TYPE

Top Will Not Operate

1. Mechanical interference due to luggage or other objects.
2. Hold down strap not removed.
3. Top not free from windshield header studs.
4. Electrical shorts or loose connections in control switch circuit.
5. Dirty control switch contacts.
6. Inoperative power unit motor.
7. Hydraulic fluid low.
8. Power unit pump inoperative.
9. Stoppage in fluid pipes.
10. Faulty hydraulic control valve.
11. Broken port plate in hydraulic pump.

Top Operates in One Direction Only

1. Mechanical interference due to luggage or other objects.
2. Hold down strap not removed.
3. Top not free from windshield header studs.
4. Electrical shorts or loose connections in control switch circuit.
5. Dirty control switch contact.
6. Improperly adjusted control rod.
7. Hydraulic power cylinder faulty.
8. Stoppage in fluid pipes.
9. Faulty hydraulic control valve.

Window Lift Inoperative

1. Mechanical interference from door arm rest screw.
2. Misaligned glass run channel or window guide.
3. Window lift not connected to lower sash channel.
4. Electrical short or loose connection in battery, motor or cylinder circuit.
5. Cylinder solenoid inoperative.
6. Power unit motor inoperative.
7. Hydraulic fluid low.
8. Hydraulic hoses crimped.
9. Stoppage in fluid pipes.
10. Pump pressure relief valve stuck.
11. Cylinder piston rod disconnected.
12. Broken port plate in pump.

Windows Operate Slowly Upward

1. Mechanical binding due to misalignment.
2. Glass run channels excessively wet.
3. If window does not fully close, stops are improperly adjusted or there is insufficient hydraulic fluid.
4. Electrical failure due to low battery.
5. Hydraulic failure due to stuck pump pressure relief valve.
6. Top control rod improperly adjusted so that control valve is held partially open to allow fluid to enter top lines.

Windows Operate Slowly Downward

1. If a window moves slowly downward when control switch is in neutral position, the solenoid valve in window lift cylinder is leaking.
2. Mechanical binding due to misalignment.
3. Glass run channels excessively wet.
4. Window lift return spring broken.
5. Hydraulic fluid old, congealed or too heavy for prevailing temperatures.
6. Pump pressure relief valve stuck.

Window Raises When Top or Seat is Operated

1. Electrical control circuit crossed due to switch "CYL" terminal touching "BAT" terminal.
2. Hydraulic pressure too high if more than one window raises.
3. Solenoid valve in window cylinder leaking.

Two Windows Operate from One Switch

1. Electrical control circuit crossed due to switch "CYL" terminals touching.
2. Hydraulic pressure too high.
3. Solenoid valve in window cylinder leaking.

Seat Adjuster Inoperative

1. Mechanical interference from object under seat.
2. Seat adjuster misaligned.
3. Seat adjuster not attached to seat frame or floor.
4. Electrical short or loose connection in battery, motor or cylinder circuit.
5. Cylinder solenoid inoperative.
6. Power unit motor inoperative.
7. Hydraulic fluid low.
8. Hydraulic hoses crimped.
9. Stoppage in fluid pipes.
10. Pump pressure relief valve stuck.
11. Cylinder piston rod disconnected.
12. Broken port plate in pump.

Seat Operates Slowly

NOTE: Same as windows operating slowly upward or downward.

All Units Operate Slowly

1. Mechanical interference due to misaligment.
2. Electrical fault due to low battery.
3. Hydraulic fluid too heavy.

4. Pump pressure relief valve stuck.
5. Crimped fluid hoses.
6. Stoppage in fluid pipes.

Power Unit Inoperative on Any Control Switch

NOTE: When running, the power unit has a clearly audible whirring sound.
1. Battery low.
2. Wiring connections between ignition switch and solenoid relay switch loose, dirty or disconnected.
3. Circuit breaker inoperative.
4. Solenoid relay switch inoperative.
5. Power unit motor inoperative.

ELECTRIC TYPE FOR WINDOWS & SEATS

NOTE: In addition to the electrical troubles listed below, look for the same mechanical troubles given under the *Hydro-Lectric Type.*

Window Won't Operate from Main Switch Only

1. Broken wire between relay and remote switch.
2. Defective switch in master switch group.
3. Break in wire where it enters door opening.

Window Won't Operate from Main or Door Switch

1. Burned out motor or relay.
2. Defective circuit breaker.
3. Break in battery feed wire from starter solenoid to circuit breaker.

Window Operates in One Direction Only from Main or Door Switch

1. Defective relay.
2. Defective switch.
3. Broken ground wires.

4. Burned out motor.
5. Broken control wire.

Circuit Breaker in Door Clicks on and off Continuously and Window Won't Operate

1. Control wire grounded.
2. Defective switch.
3. Relay points stuck.

Main or Door Switch Operates Window in Wrong Direction

1. Lead wires are not connected to proper terminals.

Window Operates Sluggishly

1. Binding window regulator.
2. Broken wires or loose connections.
3. Worn motor brushes.

All Windows Do Not Operate

1. Circuit breaker open in control circuit.
2. Circuit breaker open in power circuit.

Seat Regulators Inoperative

1. Circuit breaker open in control circuit.
2. Circuit breaker open in power circuit.

One Seat Regulator Inoperative

1. Defective wiring between relay and circuit breaker.
2. Defective motor.
3. Defective wiring between switch and circuit breaker.
4. Defective relay.

Seat Regulator Operates in One Direction Only

1. Defective wiring between switch and relay that applies to direction of travel desired.
2. Defective toggle switch.

Seat Regulator Operates Sluggishly

1. Binding mechanism.
2. Defective wiring.
3. Loose connectors or poor ground.
4. Worn or dirty brushes in motor.

▶ WINDSHIELD WIPER TROUBLES

General Inspection

Before deciding that a windshield wiper needs servicing it might be well to conisder some of the external factors which affect their operation.

It must be remembered that windshield wipers will operate more slowly when they do their own work on dry glass. This is specially true on cars with curved windshields. You will also find that wiper blades may chatter or fail to travel a complete arc on dry glass. It is therefore obvious that any testing of windshield wiper operation should be done after the windshield has been sprayed with water.

Windshield wipers that chatter or do not wipe the glass clean under normal operating conditions (wet windshield) may need only replacement of the wiper arms or blades in stead of more extensive service. This can be determined by visual inspection and most replacements can be made simply without the aid of any special tools.

Uneven movement of the wiper arms with respect to one another is usually caused by cables, pivots or cranks that are out of adjustment in the windshield wiper transmission system.

ELECTRIC TYPE

All passenger car electric windshield wiper circuits, regardless of manufacturer, include a control switch, a small shunt wound motor, and the wiring connecting these units to the battery. A circuit breaker or fuse may be mounted as a separate unit or incorporated in the control switch itself. A worm gear on the motor armature shaft drives one or two gears mounted on crankshafts for wiper operation.

A parking switch is mounted on the motor and actuated by a cam on one of the cranks. The parking switch, connected to the battery through a control switch, keeps the motor in operation for a brief period after the control switch has been shut off, allowing the wiper blades to return to the parked position.

Both single and multiple speed motors are used, the latter incorporating one or several resistors in the field circuit. The resistors may be located either in the parking switch housing or in the control switch.

In the following text you will find a list of the conditions you are likely to encounter when faced with a repair job on electric wipers. By consulting these possibilities you will simplify the job of locating the source of trouble. But before going further a few words of caution are in order: After you have made your diagnosis and are ready to make repairs, disconnect the battery to avoid damage under the dash or possible personal injury from accidental shorts. Also, on models which use off-glass parking windshield wipers, never remove or disassemble the motor while in "park" position.

Wipers Won't Operate

1. Discharged battery.
2. Blown fuse or faulty circuit breaker.
3. No power to control switch.
4. Faulty control switch.
5. Faulty parking switch.
6. Binding pivots, cranks or linkages.
7. Poor connection at switch.
8. No ground at motor.
9. Faulty motor.

Wipers Won't Park

1. Incorrect adjustment of parking switch lever.
2. Open circuit in lead feeding parking switch.

3. Faulty parking switch.
4. Faulty control switch.
5. No ground at control switch (variable speed wipers).
6. Motor crank and parking switch improperly assembled.
7. Cams in linkage reversed or binding (variable speed wipers).

Wipers Operate Slowly

1. Discharged battery.
2. Binding pivots, cranks or linkages.
3. Faulty motor windings.
4. High resistance connections or wiring.
5. High resistance in control switch contacts.
6. No ground at control switch (variable speed wipers).
7. Faulty resistance unit (if only high speed is affected).
8. Dirty commutator or sticking brushes.
9. Worn or damaged motor.

Multiple Speed Wipers Operate Only at Single Speed

1. Short or open in motor wiring harness.
2. Incorrect connections at control switch.
3. Faulty control switch.
4. Faulty resistance unit.
5. No ground at control switch.
6. Open shunt field in motor.

VACUUM TYPE

For satisfactory windshield wiper operation, it is necessary to have an adequate supply of vacuum. On some cars the vacuum is made available by tapping directly into the intake manifold. With this type of arrangement it is considered normal for the wipers to slow down or stop entirely while going up a hill or during acceleration, since under those conditions the manifold vacuum would drop below the 8″–10″ needed to operate the wipers. These conditions are almost completely eliminated on cars equipped with a vacuum booster pump. The purpose of this pump is to maintain enough vacuum to work the wipers under any driving condition.

Some of the conditions which prevent satisfactory windshield wiper operation are listed in the following text and may be used as a guide to help you locate the source of trouble. Always disconnect the battery when working under the dash.

Wipers Won't Operate

1. No vacuum supply to motor due to pinch, restriction or leak in the windshield wiper hose. A vacuum leak or a disconnected hose can easily be located because a hissing sound will be heard whenever the engine is running.
2. Faulty vacuum booster pump.
3. Wiper control switch inoperative or disconnected at motor.
4. Faulty wiper motor.
5. Frozen or binding pivots and linkages.
6. Linkages or cables improperly installed.

Wipers Operate Slowly

1. Low vacuum due to pinch or partial restriction in the wiper hose.
2. Loss of vacuum due to leaks at joints, fittings or in the wiper hose itself.
3. Faulty vacuum booster pump.
4. Faulty wiper motor.
5. Wiper control switch does not move operating valve on the motor to full "ON" position due to improper adjustment.

6. Air intake on motor (breather port) clogged.
7. Binding pivots, cranks, linkages or binding or frozen idler pulleys on cable tensioners.
8. Cables adjusted too tight.

Wipers Won't Park

1. Faulty parking valve on motor.
2. Wiper control switch out of adjustment.
3. Wiper arms not positioned properly on pivots.

PRESSURE WIPER

The windshield wiper is hydraulically operated. The hydraulic power for the motor is obtained from the power steering unit. Hydraulic fluid flows from the pump, through the steering gear to the wiper motor, and then to the fluid reservoir. During wiper operation, a part of the fluid is by-passed through the motor by a valve on the motor.

Checks and Adjustments: The only adjustment required is the control cable adjustment. To adjust, remove the seal plate mounting screws and position the plate and seal out of the way. Adjust the cable so that the control knob on instrument panel moves the valve control lever on motor from off to full on.

If the motor operates sluggishly, check the cable adjustment. If this is not the fault, check the hydraulic fluid pressure. If the power steering gear operates satisfactorily, it may be assumed that the fluid pressure is adequate. Check for binding wiper pivot shafts and arms. Repair or replace wiper motor and valves if necessary.

▶ DELCO-REMY TRANSISTORIZED IGNITION

Trouble Shooting

Faulty engine performance will usually be evidenced by engine miss, engine surge, or the engine will not run at all.

When trouble shooting the system, it is recommended that the following checks be made in the order listed.

Engine Miss

If the trouble is not due to carburetion, check the timing and the condition of the spark plugs. All the wiring should be inspected for brittle or cracked insulation, broken strands and loose or corroded connections. The high tension leads in the coil and distributor cap should be checked to make sure they are pressed all the way down in their inserts. If rubber boots are used, they too should be tightly in place over the connections. Also, the outside of the distributor cap and the coil cover should be inspected for carbonized paths which would allow high tension leakage to ground. Also, remove the distributor cap so the rotor and inside of the cap can be checked for cracks and carbonized paths.

Distributor—The pick-up coil in the distributor may be checked by separating the harness connector and connecting an ohmmeter across the coil. The resistance of the coil should be 550 to 650 ohms. If the reading is infinite (high off scale) the coil is open circuited; if the reading is low the coil is shorted. Remember that the resistance of the coil will increase slightly as the coil temperature rises.

Also, the pick-up coil may be checked for grounds by connecting the ohmmeter from either coil lead to the distributor housing. The reading should be infinite. If it is not the coil is grounded.

The distributor centrifugal and vacuum advance may be tested on a distributor testing machine. However, since this involves removing the distributor, delay this operation until after the remaining circuit checks are covered. Besides, it is not likely that the advance mechanism is the cause of the trouble.

Ignition Coil—The ignition coil primary can be checked for an open condition by connecting an ohmmeter across the two primary terminals. An infinite reading indicates the primary is open. For the engine to run but miss at times, the primary open must be of the intermittent type.

Also, the coil secondary can be checked for an open by connecting an ohmmeter from the high tension center tower to either primary terminal. To obtain a reliable reading, a scale on the ohmmeter having the 20,000 ohm value within, or nearly within, the middle third of the scale must be used. If the reading is infinite, the coil secondary winding is open. *If a coil tester is available, make sure the tester is designed to test this SPECIAL coil.*

Ignition Pulse Amplifier—If all previous checks are satisfactory, and the amplifier is properly grounded, the engine miss is probably caused by a defective ignition pulse amplifier. Replacement of the amplifier will determine if the original amplifier is defective.

Engine Surge

An engine surge condition, of a nature much more severe than that characterized by a lean carburetor mixture, may be due to the two distributor leads being reversed in the connector body, or may be due to an intermittent open in the distributor pick-up coil.

The surge condition may result from the action of the vacuum unit causing a break in the distributor pick-up coil wiring to open and close intermittently. To check this, disconnect the vacuum line and observe engine behavior at idle speed.

To complete the checks on the pick-up coil, connect an ohmmeter to the two distributor pick-up coil lead terminals in the connector body. The resistance should be 300 to 400 ohms. If the resistance is infinite the coil is open, and if the resistance is low the coil is shorted.

Also connect the ohmmeter from either terminal to the distributor housing. The reading should be infinite. If not, the winding is grounded.

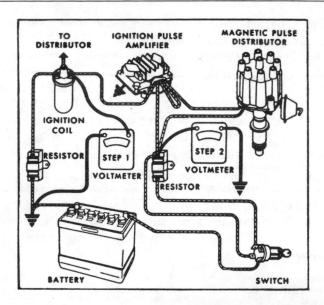

Fig. 25   Voltmeter connections for circuit checks. Delco Remy system

Engine Will Not Run

If the engine will not run at all, remove the lead from one of the spark plugs and hold it about ¼" away from the engine block while cranking the engine. If a spark occurs, the trouble most likely is not ignition. If a spark does not occur, check the distributor, wiring and ignition coil as previously described. If these check out correctly, further check the circuit continuity as follows:

  1. Connect a voltmeter as shown in Step 1, (Fig. 25). Observe reading with switch on.
      a. If reading is 8 to 9 volts, check the distributor as outlined above.
      b. If reading is battery voltage, there is an open in the circuit between this point and ground. This circuit consists of coil primary winding, resistor and wiring.

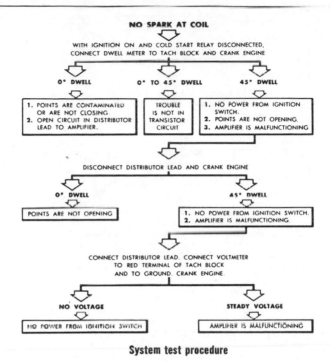

System test procedure

Fig. 20   System test procedure. 1963–65 models

c. If reading is zero, there is an open in the circuit between this point and the battery. Proceed with Step 2 as follows:

2. Connect voltmeter as shown in Step 2. Observe reading with switch on.

   a. If reading is zero there is an open between this point and the battery. This circuit consists of the resistor, ignition switch and battery.

   b. If the reading is battery voltage, there is an open in the circuit between this resistor and ignition coil. This circuit consists of ignition pulse amplifier and the wiring. If the wiring checks satisfactory, replace the amplifier.

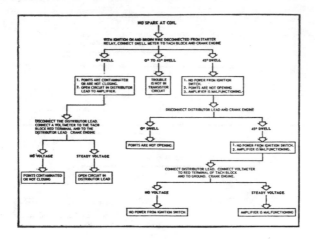

Fig. 27   System test procedures for 1966–67 models

▶ FORD TRANSISTORIZED IGNITION

CAUTION: Do not connect test equipment into the circuit in any other manner or readings will be inaccurate and damage may occur to the transistor or change its operating characteristics.

1. Remove high tension coil lead from distributor cap.
2. Disconnect brown wire from starter relay I terminal and red/blue wire from starter relay S terminal.
3. Turn on ignition switch.
4. While holding a high tension lead approximately ¼″ away from a good ground, crank engine, using an auxiliary starter switch between starter relay battery and S terminals.
5. If spark is good the trouble lies in the secondary circuit; if there is no spark or a weak spark the trouble is in the primary circuit.
6. Isolate the trouble by checking out the system as outlined on Figs. 26 and 27.

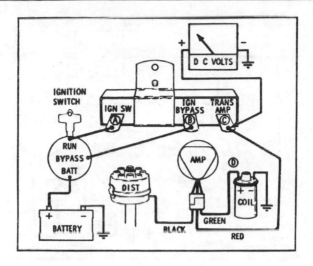

Fig. 28   Voltage check hook-up

▶ MOTOROLA SYSTEM

Trouble Shooting

Voltage Check

Fig. 28

1. With ignition on, engine not running, and distributor breaker points open, the voltmeter should read approximately 3 to 5 volts.
2. With ignition on, engine not running, and distributor breaker points closed, voltmeter should read approximately 3 to 5 volts.

NOTE: The above voltmeter readings represent average voltages and may vary from vehicle to vehicle. Some of the causes that contribute to these variations are: condition of battery, breaker points, resistance in ignition switch or wiring.

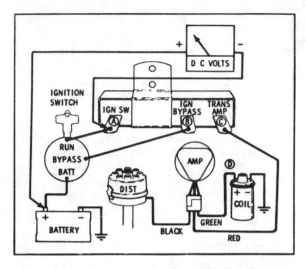

Fig. 29   Ballast resistor by-pass check hook-up

With engine running, the engine rpm and distributor dwell settings will also affect these voltage readings. However, any marked deviation from the above voltmeter readings indicate a malfunction that should be corrected.

Ballast Resistor By-Pass Check
Fig. 29

1. With ignition on, engine not running, and distributor breaker point open, voltmeter should read 0 volts.
2. With ignition on, engine not running, and distributor breaker points closed, voltmeter should read approximately 6 volts.
3. With engine on, and engine cranking, voltmeter should read approximately 1 volt or less. When the engine starts, voltmeter should read approximately 3 to 5 volts. Any marked deviation from the above voltmeter readings indicates a malfunction which should be corrected.

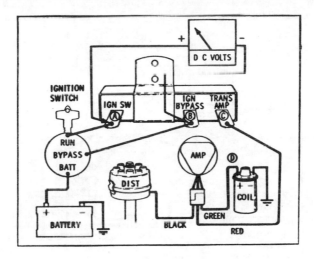

Fig. 30

Trouble Check-out

Fig. 30—With ignition on, engine not running, distributor breaker points closed, and all accessories turned off, the voltmeter should not read more than 1.5 volts. A higher voltage reading indicates that one of the following conditions exist and must be corrected.

1. Excessive resistance in the circuit from the battery through the ignition switch to the ballast resistor. Check all wiring for incorrect installation or loose connections.
2. Excessive resistance in the circuit between battery and ballast resistor will cause hard starting, poor acceleration and sluggish engine performance.

Fig. 31—With ignition on, engine not running, distributor breaker points open, and all accessories turned off, the voltmeter should read 9.5 volts or more (battery voltage) on all three ballast resistor terminals. Any marked deviation from this voltmeter reading indicates one of the following conditions may exist and must be corrected.

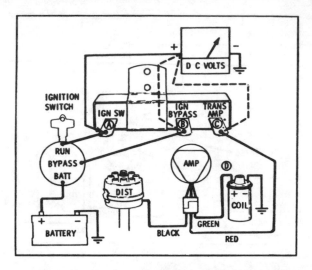

Fig. 31

1. If the correct battery voltage (9.5 volts) is present at terminal "A" of the ballast resistor, and there is no voltage at terminals "B" and "C", and the ballast resistor is cool, it indicates that the ballast resistor is defective and must be replaced.

2. If the voltage at terminal "C" is lower than the voltage at terminal "A", the cause may be one of the following:
    a) Defective wiring to distributor breaker points.
    b) Shorted transistor amplifier. Turn off ignition, disconnect the three-prong connector at amplifier. Turn ignition on. If voltage at terminal "C" is now the same as terminal "A", the transistor amplifier is defective and must be replaced.
    c) If voltage at terminal "C" is still not the same as terminal "A", the installation may be incorrect. Check all wiring connections and be sure there are no other connections at the ballast resistor other than what is shown in Fig. 31.

d) With the amplifier unplugged, disconnect wiring connector from terminal "B" at ballast resistor. If voltage at terminal "C" is now the same as terminal "A", the ignition by-pass wiring is defective. If the voltage at terminal "C" is still lower than at terminal "A", the ballast resistor is defective and must be replaced.

Fig. 28—With ignition on, engine not running and distributor breaker points closed, the voltmeter should read approximately 3 to 5 volts. If the voltmeter reads 9.5 volts or more (battery voltage), the fault may be caused by one of the following conditions:

1. Distributor breaker points not closing or defective wiring to breaker points.
2. Defective transistor amplifier or ignition coil. Measure voltage at positive terminal of ignition coil (D). If voltmeter reads 9.5 volts or more (battery voltage), the ignition coil is improperly grounded or defective. If zero voltage is indicated at this point (D), the transistor amplifier is defective and must be replaced.
3. If the voltmeter reads zero volts at the transistor amplifier terminal (C) of the ballast resistor, and the ballast resistor is cool, the ballast resistor is defective and must be replaced.

NOTE: If all voltages read as specified in the check-out and trouble procedures, the ignition coil should be checked. This can be done by substituting a known good Motorola coil in the circuit.

▶ AIR CONDITIONING

NOTE: When a unit must be removed from the system for replacement or repairs, the dehydrator must be replaced also, and the system must be purged, evacuated and recharged to remove excess moisture.

SYSTEM PRODUCES NO COOLING

Electrical

1. Blown fuse.
2. Disconnected or broken wire.
3. Clutch coil disconnected or burned out.
4. Switch contacts in thermostat (if used) burned excessively, or sensing element defective.
5. Blower motor burned out or disconnected.

Mechanical

1. Loose or broken drive belt.
2. Compressor completely or partially frozen.
3. Compressor reed valves inoperative.
4. Expansion valve stuck open.

Refrigeration

1. Broken refrigeration line.
2. Fusable plug blown (if used).
3. Leak in system.
4. Compressor shaft seal leaking.
5. Clogged screen or screens in receiver-dehydrator or expansion valve.
6. Plugged coil or hose.

INSUFFICIENT COOLING

Electrical

1. Blower motor operates sluggishly.

Mechanical

1. Compressor clutch slipping.
2. Obstructed blower discharge passage.
3. Clogged air intake filter.
4. Outside air vents open.
5. Insufficient air circulation over condenser coils; fins clogged with dirt, leaves or insects.
6. Evaporator clogged.

7. Evaporator regulator defective or improperly adjusted.

NOTE: The evaporator regulator includes the hot gas by-pass valve used on most General Motors cars prior to 1962, suction throttling control valve (STV) used on 1962–65 General Motors cars, the Pilot Operated Absolute (POA) valve used on 1966–67 General Motors cars, and the Chrysler Evaporator Pressure Regulator (EPR) valve. When any of these devices are used in a system, it can be assumed that the system contains no thermostat-control.

Refrigeration

1. Insufficient refrigerant in system.
2. Clogged screen in expansion valve.
3. Expansion valve thermal bulb has lost its charge.
4. Clogged screen in receiver.
5. Excessive moisture in system.
6. Air in system.
7. Thermostat defective or improperly adjusted (if used).

SYSTEM COOLS INTERMITTENTLY

Electrical

1. Defective circuit breaker, blower switch or blower motor.
2. Partial open, improper ground or loose connection in compressor clutch coil.

Mechanical

1. Compressor clutch slipping.

Refrigeration

1. Unit icing up; may be caused by excessive moisture in system, incorrect superheat adjustment in expansion valve, or thermostat adjusted too low (if used).

2. Thermostat defective (if used).
3. Stuck hot gas by-pass valve, STV, POA or EPR valve.

▶ AUTOMATIC LEVEL CONTROL

GENERAL MOTORS

Car Loaded, Will Not Rise

1. External damage or breakage.
2. Line leak.
3. Linkage to overtravel lever in wrong hole.
4. Control valve setting incorrect.
5. Defective component.

Car Loaded, Raises to Level, Then Leaks Down

1. Line leak.
2. Control valve exhaust leak.
3. Superlift leak.
4. Control valve leak.

Car Loaded, Raises Partially

1. Load excessive (over 500 lbs. at axle) on cars with special springs.
2. Control valve setting incorrect.
3. Low supply pressure.

Car Unloaded, Rides too High, Will Not Come Down

1. Control valve setting incorrect.
2. Improper springs.
3. External damage or breakage.
4. Linkage to overtravel in wrong hole.
5. Defective control valve.

Car Rises When Loaded but Leaks Down While Driving

1. Time delay mechanism not functioning properly.

FORD MOTOR COMPANY

Vehicle Loaded, Will Not Raise

1. External damage or breakage.
2. Line or cylinder leak.
3. Pump inoperative or output inadequate.
4. Control valve setting incorrect.
5. Inadequate time delay.

Vehicle Loaded, Raises Partially

1. Load excessive (over 250 lbs.) at axle.
2. Height control valve setting incorrect.
3. Low supply pressure.

Vehicle Unloaded, Rides too High, Won't Come Down

1. Control valve setting incorrect.
2. External damage or breakage.
3. Defective control valve.

Compressor Cycles Continuously

1. Line leak.
2. Air cylinder ruptured.
3. Inadequate time; may take five minutes to balance at idle.

Compressor Does Not Cycle

1. Vacuum hose off or leaking.
2. Pump internal failure.
3. Lines or hoses restricted.
4. Pump filter clogged.

Vehicle Loaded, Raises to Level and Then Leaks Down

1. Line leak.
2. Control valve exhaust leak.
3. Air cylinder leak.
4. Control valve exhaust leak.
5. If leak down while driving, check for control valve time delay less than one second.

▶ CONCEALED HEADLAMPS

Vacuum Type

Examine all hoses for splits, which occur most often around connections. Also, look for kinked or pinched hoses, a condition which often occurs when retaining clips are too tight, thus blocking off vacuum flow.

If inspection reveals that all the hoses are satisfactory, check each vacuum actuator by disconnecting the actuator hoses one at a time and hooking a vacuum gauge to the hose(s). With engine running, if the gauge indicates at least 14 inches of vacuum, the problem is either in the actuator, which must be replaced, or because of jammed covers or linkage.

If the gauge shows less than 14 inches of vacuum, check vacuum at the storage tank, distribution valve, check valve vacuum relay, if used, and at each hose connection.

Electrical Type

Connect a jumper wire directly from the battery to the motor(s). If the system operates, check the headlight or motor control switch. If the switch is eliminated as the cause of trouble, check the wiring; look for loose connections, broken wires or terminals.

If the system fails to operate with the jumper wire, remove the motor for repair or install a new or rebuilt unit.

▶ SPEED CONTROLS
GENERAL MOTORS A.C. ELECTRO-CRUISE

No Action when Engagement Switch Knob is Depressed

1. Broken connection.
2. Blown fuses.
3. Brake release switch out of adjustment.
4. Vacuum leak.
5. Power unit coil open.
6. Defective transistor amplifier.

Cruise Lamp Lights When Knob is Depressed with No Response

1. Harness to speedometer unplugged or loose.
2. Defective contacts on speed transducer.

Cruise Lamp Lights When Knob is Depressed Below 3 MPH of Set Speed

1. Harness to speedometer loose.
2. Defective contacts on speed transducer.

System Remains Engaged When Brake Pedal is Depressed

1. Brake release switch out of adjustment.
2. Shorted brake release switch.
3. Shorted wire harness in cruise release line.

Blows Fuses

1. Shorted wiring.
2. Shorted differential relay, cruise telltale light or power unit coil.
3. Shorted transistor amplifier.

Engine Races When Started When Engage Button is Not Pushed

1. Shorted wiring harness.
2. Shorted engage switch.
3. Shorted differential relay.
4. Vacuum orifice leak in power unit.
5. Accelerator linkage bound up.

Will Not Lock In After Set Speed is Attained

1. Defective differential relay.

Keeps Accelerating Up Past Set Speed

1. Shorted wire harness.
2. Shorted contacts on Cruise speedometer.
3. Defective differential relay.

System Automatically Locks In on Rough Roads

1. Defective differential relay.
2. Loose connection.
3. Brake release switch set too tight.

System Drops Out Over Rough Roads

1. Defective differential relay.
2. Loose connection.
3. Brake release switch set too tight.

Erratic Cruise Speed

1. Loose connection.
2. Defective contacts on Cruise speedometer.
3. Armature in power unit hanging up.
4. Vacuum leak.

Slow Response

1. Vacuum leak.

Hunts at Slow Speeds

1. Erratic Cruise speedometer.
2. Excessive slack in ball chain.
3. Stiff accelerator linkage.
4. Vacuum leak.
5. Dragging brakes.

Does Not Disengage When Knob is Pulled

1. Shorted wire harness.
2. Shorted engagement switch.
3. Defective differential relay.

Hissing Noise When Engine is Running

1. Vacuum leak.

Indicator Lamp Does Not Light

1. Lamp socket not plugged in.
2. Burned out tell-tale lamp.

3. Defective differential relay.
4. Broken wire harness.

Car Won't Idle When System is Not Engaged

1. Vacuum leak.
2. Ball chain adjusted too tightly.

Will Not Reach High Cruise Speeds

1. Excessive slack in ball chain.
2. Beyond capabilities of engine due to extremely high altitude and/or excessive road grades.
3. Defective speedometer.

Pointer & Odometer Does Not Record

1. Broken flexible shaft.
2. Defective speedometer.

Cruise Pointer & Speedometer Do Not Coincide When in Cruise

1. Stiff throttle linkage.
2. Cruise speedometer out of calibration.
3. Wrong throttle return spring.
4. Vacuum leak.

Excessive Power Unit Noise

1. Wrong or no sound dampening cushion between power unit and fire wall.
2. Worn or defective power unit armature.
3. Power unit mounting screws too tight.

Pedal Noise When in Cruise

1. Worn accelerator linkage or pedal.
2. Accelerator pedal hinge stiff or worn.

Excessive Overshoot Condition

1. Defective speed transducer.
2. Tight throttle linkage.

3. Vacuum leak.
4. Dragging brakes.

Whistling Noise When Brake or Clutch Pedal is Touched

1. Dirty or worn brake release switch.
2. Foreign matter in cruise release line.

▶ CHRYSLER AUTO PILOT

NOTE: It is recommended that the diagnosis be performed in the sequence given. If the trouble proves to be internal in the Auto Pilot drive mechanism, Chrysler recommends that the unit be replaced.

Control Button Does Not Remain Out with Ignition On

1. Blown fuse.
2. Poor electrical connections to control.
3. Faulty control.

No "Speed Warning" Pedal Pressure

1. Blown fuse or faulty wiring in motor circuit (red wire).
2. Accelerator linkage broken or disconnected.

"Speed Warning" Pedal Pressure at All Speeds

1. Faulty electrical circuit.

Automatic Latching Does Not Engage When Button is Pulled Out

1. Not enough brake switch clearance.
2. Brake pedal not returning fully.
3. Faulty electrical circuit.

Automatic Latch Engages at Selected Speed with Button Pushed In

1. No. 3 black wire to panel control is grounded.
2. Faulty grounding switch in instrument panel control.

Automatic Latch Remains Engaged when Brake Pedal is Touched

1. Faulty or improperly adjusted brake switch.

Unit Disengages Intermittently on Rough Roads

1. Poor electrical connections.
2. Not enough brake switch clearance.

Will Not Function at Low End of Dial

1. Improper control cable adjustment.

Pulsating Accelerator Pedal

1. Speedometer cable or drive cable kinked.
2. Lack of cable lubrication.
3. Improper accelerator linkage adjustment.

Carburetor Does Not Return to Normal Idle

1. Improper Auto Pilot linkage adjustment.
2. Standard throttle linkage faulty.

Speedometer Does Not Register or Operate

1. Speedometer drive pinion in transmission is faulty.
2. Faulty speedometer cable.
3. Faulty drive cable from transmission to Auto Pilot drive mechanism.
4. Faulty speedometer.

Speedometer Noise

1. Cables bent or kinked.
2. Lack of cable lubrication.
3. Noisy speedometer head.

Fuses Blow Repeatedly

1. Short circuit in wiring, drive mechanism or switches.

SLIDE SWITCH TYPE TROUBLES

Speedometer Noise

1. Cables bent or kinked.
2. Lack of cable lubrication.
3. Noisy speedometer head.

Fuses Blow Repeatedly

1. Short or ground in wiring circuit.
2. Defective motor.
3. Lacked drive screw.

No Speed Control Response

1. Accelerator linkage broken or disconnected.
2. Drive cables broken or disconnected.
3. Blown fuse.
4. Loose connection or broken wires (internal or external).

No Automatic Control When Unit is Set
for Automatic Lock-In

1. Driver riding brake pedal or does not accelerate to selected speed.
2. No current at No. 2 terminal.
3. Improper throttle switch adjustment.
4. Improper brake release switch adjustment.

Constant Pressure on Accelerator Pedal
Regardless of Dial Setting

1. Blown fuse.
2. No current at No. 1 terminal.
3. Control cable improperly adjusted.
4. Control cable defective.
5. Inoperative motor or locked drive screw.
6. Improper limit switch adjustment.

Automatic Control Engages at Selected Speed
Without Unit Set for Automatic Lock-In

1. Improper brake release switch adjustment or defective switch.

Unit Does Not Remain Inoperative in "Off" Position

1. Limit switch not properly adjusted.

Pulsating Accelerator Pedal

1. Speedometer cable or drive cable kinked or lack lubrication.
2. Improper accelerator linkage adjustment.
3. Improper motor feed points adjustment.

Carburetor Does Not Return to Normal Idle

1. Improper carburetor or accelerator linkage adjustment.
2. Weak or disconnected throttle return spring.

Unit Does Not Control at Selected Speed

1. Improper control cable adjustment.
2. Improper selector dial adjustment.
3. Improper accelerator linkage adjustment.

Unit Controls at Low Speed Regardless of Selector Setting

1. Control cable not secured to selector coupling.

Speedometer Does Not Register

1. Transmission drive gear in transmission defective.
2. Broken drive cable from transmission to power unit.
3. Damaged drive gear or nylon gear in power unit.
4. Broken speedometer cable.

▶ FORD MARQUETTE SYSTEM (EXC. 1966–67 T-BIRD)

Engine Won't Return to Normal Idle

1. Throttle linkage not properly adjusted.
2. Speed control accelerator linkage improperly adjusted.

Vehicle Over-Speeds Speed Setting

1. Pressure hose between sensor pump and metering valve leaking.
2. Defective metering valve diaphragm.
3. Vacuum hoses to metering valve reversed.

Increase in Minimum Controllable Speed

1. Loss of fluid from sensor pump.

Dial Speed Setting Does Not Correspond to Speedometer Reading

1. Improper control cable adjustment.

High Engagement Speed Over Set Speed

1. Contact points in metering valve too far apart.

System Resumes Speed After Depressing and Releasing Brake Pedal or Resumes Speed Well Below Set Speed

1. Metering valve contact points too close or fused together.
2. Shorted resume-speed button or wiring.

Control Button Won't Stay Out, System Inoperative

1. Blown fuse.
2. Wire off back of switch or ignition, or wiring is defective.
3. Switch button burned out.

Control Button Stays Out, System Inoperative

1. Any of system components.

Control Engages Below Desired Speed

1. Resume-speed switch shorted.
2. Metering valve points shorted.
3. Wiring shorted.

Control Won't Resume when Resume Switch is Activated

1. Resume-speed switch defective.
2. Switch not properly grounded.
3. Wire off back of switch or defective wiring.

Control Will Not Disengage when Brake Pedal is Depressed

1. Brake switch not properly adjusted or defective.

Control Inoperative, Speedometer Does Not Register

1. Broken speedometer cable between transmission and sensor pump.

Control Operates but Speedometer Does Not Register

1. Broken speedometer cable between sensor pump and speedometer.
2. Inoperative speedometer mechanism.

Speed Continuously Changes Up and Down

1. Vacuum hose split between intake manifold of engine and vacuum valve, between vacuum valve and metering valve or between metering valve and vacuum bellows.
2. Ruptured vacuum bellows.
3. Defective metering valve.
4. Sticky carburetor or accelerator linkage.

System Sluggish, Won't Hold Speed on Hills

1. Ball chain between vacuum bellows and accelerator not properly adjusted.

2. Defective sensor pump.
3. Sticky carburetor or accelerator linkage.
4. Vacuum leak in hoses.
5. Leak in vacuum bellows.

▶ FORD MARQUETTE SYSTEM 1966–67 T-BIRD

Switch Button Won't Stay Out, System Inoperative

1. Fuse blown.
2. Wire on back of switch button off or defective wiring.
3. Switch button burned out.

Switch Button Stays Out, System Inoperative

1. Defective electrical circuit.
2. Rubber tube between sensor pump and metering valve or inhibitor switch off or leaking.
3. Fluid low or gone from sensor pump.
4. Ruptured vacuum bellows.
5. Vacuum bellows disconnected from accelerator linkage.
6. Brake release relay or wiring defective.
7. Defective lock-in valve.

Speed Continuously Changes Up and Down

1. Vacuum hose split between engine intake manifold and vacuum valve, between vacuum valve and metering valve, or between metering valve and vacuum bellows.
2. Ruptured vacuum bellows.
3. Defective metering valve.
4. Sticky carburetor or accelerator linkage.

System Does Not Retard With Retard Switch Pressed

1. Defective retard switch in steering wheel.
2. Wire disconnected or defective at brake retard vacuum valve.

265

3. Defective brake retard valve.
4. Vacuum line split or off between vacuum reservoir and brake retard vacuum valve or brake retard vacuum valve and vacuum motor.
5. Ruptured brake retard vacuum motor.
6. Brake retard vacuum motor disconnected from brake pedal bracket.
7. Ball chain not adjusted properly.

System Sluggish, Won't Hold Speed on Hills

1. Defective sensor pump.
2. Sticky carburetor or accelerator linkage.
3. Vacuum leak in hoses, vacuum bellows or kinked vacuum hoses.

Low Speed Setting Too High

1. Rubber tube between sensor pump and inhibitor switch or metering valve leaking.

System Retains Memory after Engine is Turned Off and then Restarted

1. Defective or disconnected wiring between starter relay and control relay.

Speed Control Remains Engaged when Brake is Depressed or Retard Switch is Pressed

1. Defective brake pedal pad switch.
2. Defective vacuum switch.
3. Vacuum leak in retard system.

System Inoperative, Speedometer Does Not Register

1. Speedometer cable broken between transmission and sensor pump.
2. Defective speedometer drive or driven gear.

System Operative but Speedometer Does Not Register

1. Speedometer cable between sensor pump and speedometer broken.
2. Defective speedometer head.

EXCESSIVE FUEL CONSUMPTION

Complaints of excessive fuel consumption require a careful investigation of the owner's driving habits and operating conditions as well as the mechanical condition of the engine and fuel system; otherwise much needless work may be done in an attempt to increase fuel economy.

Driving habits which seriously affect fuel economy are: high speed driving, frequent and rapid acceleration, driving too long in low and second speed when getting underway, excessive idling while standing.

Operating conditions which adversely affect fuel economy are: excessive acceleration, frequent starts and stops, congested traffic, poor roads, hills and mountains, high winds, low tire pressures.

High speed is the greatest contributor to low gas mileage. Air resistance increases as the square of speed. For instance, a car going 60 miles an hour must overcome air resistance four times as great as when going 30 miles an hour. At 80 miles an hour the resistance is over seven times as great as when going 30 miles an hour. Over 75 per cent of the power required to drive a car 80 miles an hour is used in overcoming air resistance, while at 30 miles an hour only 30 per cent of the power required is used to overcome air resistance.

Gas mileage records made by car owners never give a true picture of the efficiency of the engine fuel system since they include the effects of driving habits and operating conditions. Because of the wide variation in these conditions, it is impossible to give average mileage figures for cars in general use. Therefore, any investigation of a mileage complaint must be based on an accurate measurement of gasoline consumption per mile under proper test conditions.

Gasoline Mileage Test

There are a number of gasoline mileage testers commercially available that measure fuel consumption precisely. Manufacturers of these devices furnish full instructions for their use. However, an inexpensive tester can be made with a quart oil can, suitable fittings and a tube to connect the can to the carburetor.

Drill or punch a hole in the bottom of the can and solder a fitting to the hole. The fitting at the carburetor end should be the same as the existing fitting at the carburetor inlet. Arrange a suitable handle or wire hook to the can so it can be mounted either under the hood or in the driver's compartment.

Before making the test, disconnect the fuel pipe at the carburetor and plug the pipe opening with a small cork so that the fuel will not spurt out during the test. Run the engine until all the fuel in the carburetor is used up. Then connect the tester tube to the carburetor.

With the can mounted at a higher level than the carburetor so fuel will flow into the carburetor by gravity, pour exactly one quart of gasoline into the can.

Make the test on a reasonably level road, at fixed speeds, without acceleration or deceleration. Test runs should be made in both directions over the same stretch of road to average the effect of grade and wind resistance. Test runs made at 30, 50, and 70 miles an hour will indicate the approximate efficiency of the low speed, high speed and power systems of the carburetor and show whether fuel consumption is actually abnormal. Under the conditions given, the fuel consumption in miles per gallon, based on the normal economy of a car capable of giving 20 miles per gallon at 20 miles per hour, should be approximately as follows:

Constant Speed	Miles per Gal.
20	20.0
30	19.7
50	15.9
70	8.0

If it takes 5 miles to empty the can, it means that the fuel consumption is 20 miles per gallon, since there are 4 quarts to the gallon.

If the test indicates that the fuel consumption is above normal, check the following before deciding to take the carburetor apart:

1. Check all gasoline pipe connections, fuel pump bowl gasket, gasoline filter gasket, and carburetor bowl gasket.
2. Check for low tire pressures.

3. Check for dragging brakes.
4. Late ignition timing causes loss of power and increases fuel consumption. Dirty or worn out spark plugs are wasteful of fuel.
5. Use of gasoline of such low grade that ignition timing must be retarded to avoid excessive detonation will give very poor fuel economy.
6. Check for sticking manifold heater valve or improper setting of the thermostat.
7. Check for dirty or clogged air cleaner element and for excessive oil in the crankcase.
8. Check for sticking choke valve and improper setting of the automatic choke thermostat.
9. Check for insufficient valve operating clearance or sticking valve.
10. Check for excessive fuel pump pressure.
11. Check for carburetor idle adjustment. On Carter carburetors, the metering rod setting may be checked without removing the carburetor. For all other corrections to high speed and power systems on all carburetors, the carburetor must be removed and disassembled.

Changing Carburetor Jets

Under no circumstances should leaner than standard jet sizes, metering rods and other calibrations of a carburetor be changed from factory specifications. The specified calibrations must be adhered to unless these are later changed by a bulletin issued by the carburetor manufacturer.

Carburetor calibrations have been determined by exhaustive tests with laboratory equipment and instruments which accurately measure overall performance and economy. Besides, the leanest possible mixture obtainable by the use of smaller jets, etc., will not increase mileage as much as 10 per cent, and will often impair engine performance.

TRIP PLANNING

Many a well planned vacation trip has been turned into a near nightmare because the planning did not take into consideration that all too often the automobile that was to take you broke down on the way. This surprise element becomes even more important today when so many people are taking campers and trailers far off the main arteries and into the backwoods where help is hard to find if an emergency arises.

With this in mind, the Editors have tried here to outline an emergency repair kit consisting of essential tools and parts which the average motorist might have a need for. It should be kept in mind though, whenever a trip is contemplated it would be wise to have the automobile properly serviced before starting. In short, the best remedy for an emergency is to take all precautions necessary to prevent its occurrence. Your local service station may even suggest items we might have overlooked.

To be able to deal properly with the most common emergencies, we suggest you build a kit consisting of screwdrivers, ignition wrenches, pliers, spark plug wrench, booster cables, flares, reflectors, first aid kit, flashlight, fire extinguisher and a block and tackle or similar equipment to help pull you out of a ditch. Some of these items may seem a bit far fetched, but remember, even though you might not be acquainted with the use of some of these tools, they should be available in the event someone more talented happens along and offers his help.

To the above list you should also add a siphon hose and a safe container suitable for carrying gasoline. You may not want to carry a full can of gasoline with you but if you have ever run out of gas on the road you know how difficult it is to pry a can away from the station operator without leaving a deposit and then there is always the chance someone else may come along and permit you to siphon some gas from his tank.

In the spare parts kit be sure to have a fan belt, radiator hoses and clamps, fuses, ignition points, condenser, rotor, engine oil, transmission fluid, which can also be used in power steering pumps, and spark plugs. This modest investment will not be wasted because even though you may not need the parts on your trip they can be used at the next regular servicing of your car.

Of course, even though we have not mentioned it, be sure you have a good operating jack and wooden blocks or chocks for the wheels.

A pair of coveralls, wiping cloths and a hand cleaner will help to brighten the remainder of your journey.

Check List

- ☐ First aid kit
- ☐ Fire extinguisher
- ☐ Booster cables
- ☐ Safe container for gas
- ☐ Flashlight
    (check batteries)
- ☐ Reflectors and flares
- ☐ Screwdrivers
    (blade and phillips)
- ☐ Ignition wrenches
- ☐ Feeler gauge
- ☐ Pliers

- ☐ Spark plug wrench
- ☐ Block & tackle
- ☐ Tow rope
- ☐ Tire pump
- ☐ Jack
- ☐ Wooden blocks
    or chocks
- ☐ Siphon hose
- ☐ Fan belt
- ☐ Radiator hoses
    and clamps
- ☐ Fuses

- ☐ Engine oil
- ☐ Trans fluid
- ☐ Ignition points,
    condenser, rotor
- ☐ Spark plugs
- ☐ Tire/tube repair kit
- ☐ Hammer
- ☐ Spare keys

DEFINITION OF TERMS

Bore and Stroke

Bore is the diameter of the cylinder in inches.

Stroke is the distance the piston moves between upper and lower dead center in inches.

Piston Displacement

Piston displacement for one cylinder is the cubic volume through which the piston sweeps in moving the length of one stroke. This volume in cubic inches multiplied by the number of cylinders gives the piston displacement of the whole engine. This total piston displacement indicates the "size" of the engine. Piston displacement may be figured by means of the following simple formula:

Piston displacement equals bore × bore
× stroke × number of cylinders × .785.

All other things being equal, the piston displacement of an engine is an index of the power it may be expected to produce.

Engine Torque

Engine torque or turning effort is the rotating force developed at the flywheel. In the case of a typical automobile engine this force might be 200 pounds when measured at a radius of one foot from the center of the flywheel. When the torque radius is one foot it is customary to say that the torque developed by an engine is 200 pounds-feet. This term should not be confused with foot-pounds although there is a relationship between them, namely one pound-foot of torque during one revolution represents 6.28 foot-pounds of mechanical energy.

Brake Horsepower

Brake horsepower is the actual horsepower of the engine delivered at the flywheel. Many years ago it was customary to measure horsepower by a device called a Prony brake (named after the man who invented it)—hence the term brake horsepower. Today, however, horsepower is determined by a dynamometer of which there are several types. Both the Prony brake and the dynamometer measure torque. The horsepower is calculated from the torque.

By definition one horsepower represents the production of 33,000 foot-pounds of mechanical energy per minute. Therefore horsepower equals foot-pounds per minute divided by 33,000. Foot pounds may be defined as the mechanical energy developing by a force of so many pounds acting through a certain distance per minute. Thus a force of, say, 33,000 pounds acting through a distance of ten feet in one minute would represent 330,000 foot-pounds or 10 hp (330,000/33,000).

When an engine is tested on a dynamometer, if it develops 200 pounds-feet of torque it delivers 200 × 6.28 foot-pounds of mechanical energy per revolution or 1256 foot-puonds (200 × 6.28).

If the engine is running 1,000 rpm, the foot-pound production per minute is 1,256,000 foot-pounds (1256 × 1,000) or 38 hp (1,256,000/33,000).

The torque is measured at various other engine speeds from, say, 500 to 4,000 rpm and the horsepower for each speed is calculated.

Taxable Horsepower

In some states, automobiles are taxed according to a taxable horsepower rating based on the following formula:

Taxable horsepower equals bore ×
bore × number of cylinders × .4.

This ancient formula was fairly true 40 years ago but has no relationship to the horsepower production of modern engines. The taxable horsepower formula is often called the S.A.E. horsepower formula but the Society of Automotive Engineers had nothing to do with it. The formula was originated by The Royal Automobile Club of England.

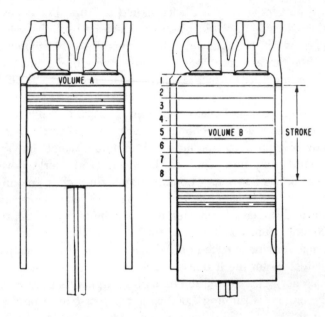

Fig. 1   The compression ratio of this engine is 8 to 1 since volume B is
8 times volume A

Compression Ratio

Compression ratio is the ratio between the total volume of the interior of a cylinder with the piston at bottom dead center divided by the volume at top dead center, Fig. 1. For example, in a given engine the total volume with piston at bottom dead center might be 80 cubic inches while the volume at top center might be 10 cubic inches, in which case the compression ratio would be 8 to 1 (80/10). Piston displacement is the difference between these two volumes of 70 cubic inches.

Another way of expressing compression ratio is as follows: Determine the volume of the combustion chamber with piston at top dead center—say this volume is 10 cubic inches for example and that the calculated piston displacement is 70 cubic inches.

Therefore the compression ratio is

$$\frac{10 + 70}{10} - \frac{8}{1}$$

Compression ratios on modern cars range from 7.50 to 1 up to 11.0 or more. Power and fuel economy are increased as the compression ratio is raised.

Other things being equal, the higher the compression ratio the higher the *compression pressure* obtained at the end of the compression stroke. Compression pressures on modern cars range roughly from 110 to 200 pounds per square inch on open throttle. In a given make and model of engine, compression pressure is a maximum some certain speed, say, 1,800 rpm, for example. Above and below this speed the compression pressure falls off gradually. Maximum torque is produced when compression pressure is at maximum. Compression pressure is reduced as the throttle is closed, being about 35 pounds at idling speed.

When the spark ignites the mixture, combustion should proceed smoothly in expanding circles, Fig. 2, until all the mixture in the combustion chamber is consumed. Pressure in the combustion chamber rises as combustion proceeds and reaches a maximum about the time all of the mixture is burned. The higher the compression pressure the greater the maximum combustion pressure.

Detonation

The preceding paragraph describes normal combustion. However, under certain conditions, after combustion has proceeded part way through the chamber, the remaining mixture may go off with a bang like so much dynamite. This explosion causes a sharp rise in pressure which shakes the cylinder head and causes the head to vibrate with the result that a metallic knock is heard. The phenomenon just described is called *detonation*. Detonation (pinging) occurs only when the throttle is wide open or nearly so and it is more likely to occur at moderate engine speed (15 to 20 mph) than at high engine speed.

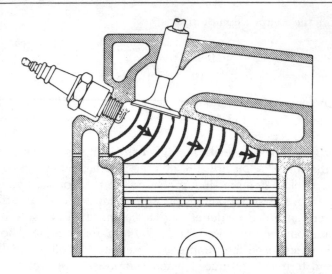

Fig. 2   The progress of combustion is indicated by the expanding circles
radiating from the spark plug points

There are certain factors that encourage detonation and others
that discourage or completely eliminate it. Factors that encourage
detonation include high compression pressure resulting from high
compression ratio. A hot spot in the combustion chamber such as
an unduly hot exhaust valve, piston head, cylinder head, and so
forth. Severe detonation will be heard when the cooling water is
boiling in the cylinder head or when there is no water in the
head. A heavy coating of carbon on cylinder head or piston head
may cause detonation. The carbon prevents adequate cooling of
the surfaces and thus detonation is encouraged. Carbon also increases the compression ratio which in turn encourages detonation. If the spark occurs too early as the piston moves upward on
its compression stroke, detonation will result. All the factors
mentioned in this paragraph including high compression pressure
increase the temperature of the mixture and the higher the mixture temperature the greater is the tendency to detonate. Also, the
lower the octane number of the fuel the more likely it is that

detonation will take place. A lean mixture encourages detonation.

On the other hand, detonation can be satifactorily suppressed or eliminated by using a sufficiently high octane fuel; by reducing the compression pressure; by timing the spark so that it occurs at the proper instant rather than too soon; by keeping the combustion chamber surfaces adequately cool, and free of carbon.

Usually detonation does not occur until most of mixture has been burned. Therefore, if this mixture is cooled somewhat its detonation is avoided. Cooling this last portion of the mixture is obtained by suitable combustion chamber design. In the case of the combustion chamber shown in Fig. 2, by the time the flame front has reached the valve area the burned gases have a pressure of 400 to 600 pounds per square inch and that therefore the remaining unburned gas has likewise been compressed to this high figure. Therefore, the remaining mixture is quite hot because mixture temperature increases with pressure. But then the mixture encounters the comparatively cool cylinder head and piston head where its temperature is reduced below the detonating point. The same result can be obtained by bulging the piston head upward, so that the last portion of the mixture to burn is forced into close contact with the cylinder head and piston head, and in this way the remaining mixture is cooled below the detonation point.

Spark Knock and Pre-Ignition

Spark knock, as previously indicated, is caused by allowing the spark to occur too early. Pre-ignition is caused by a red hot spot in the combustion chamber. Such a spot might be a piece of carbon which is hot enough to ignite the mixture before the spark occurs, or a red hot spark plug, red hot exhaust valve or gasket edge too hot.

NOTES

NOTES

NOTES